SONG OF THE FOREST

Books by Ruskin Bond

Fiction

The Shadow on the Wall: My Favourite Stories of Ghosts, Spirits, and Things that Go Bump in the Night
Miracle at Happy Bazaar: My Very Best Stories for Children
Rhododendrons in the Mist: My Favourite Tales of the Himalaya
A Gallery of Rascals: My Favourite Tales of Rogues, Rapscallions and Ne'er-do-wells
Unhurried Tales: My Favourite Novellas
Small Towns, Big Stories
Upon an Old Wall Dreaming
A Gathering of Friends
Tales of Fosterganj
The Room on the Roof & Vagrants in the Valley
The Night Train at Deoli and Other Stories
Time Stops at Shamli and Other Stories
Our Trees Still Grow in Dehra
A Season of Ghosts
When Darkness Falls and Other Stories
A Flight of Pigeons
Delhi Is Not Far
A Face in the Dark and Other Hauntings
The Sensualist
A Handful of Nuts
Maharani
Secrets

Non-fiction

It's a Wonderful Life: Roads to Happiness
Rain in the Mountains
Scenes from a Writer's Life
Landour Days
Notes from a Small Room
The India I Love

Anthologies

A Town Called Dehra
Classic Ruskin Bond: Complete and Unabridged
Classic Ruskin Bond Volume 2: The Memoirs
Dust on the Mountain: Collected Stories
Friends in Small Places
Ghost Stories from the Raj
Great Stories for Children
Tales of the Open Road
The Essential Collection for Young Readers
Ruskin Bond's Book of Nature
Ruskin Bond's Book of Humour
The Writer on the Hill

Poetry

Hip-Hop Nature Boy & Other Poems
Ruskin Bond's Book of Verse

SONG OF THE FOREST

TALES FROM HERE, THERE, AND EVERYWHERE

RUSKIN BOND

ALEPH

ALEPH BOOK COMPANY
An independent publishing firm
promoted by *Rupa Publications India*

First published in India in 2022
by Aleph Book Company
7/16 Ansari Road, Daryaganj
New Delhi 110 002

ISBN: 978-93-91047-68-9

3 5 7 9 10 8 6 4 2

Printed in India

CONTENTS

FOREWORD
A LONG RIVER OF SHORT STORIES

Ruskin Bond is that rarest of writers, one who is able to write short and long stories (or novellas) and novels with equal facility. It's rather like being ambidextrous—it's extremely rare to find someone who can use both hands with the same dexterity without favouring either the right hand or the left. Ruskin made his mark on the literary world with his extraordinary first novel, *The Room on the Roof*, over half a century ago, but in the intervening decades it's been his short fiction, the author's favourite literary form, that has appeared at regular intervals and captivated generations of readers.

What makes for a successful short story? To explain that, let me quote from a book that I read recently that attempts to describe what a short story is—beyond the befuddling ideas and jargon imposed on the form by people who have probably never written short fiction themselves but claim to know all about it, usually literary critics or university professors who teach literature. This definition of short fiction is taken from the latest work by

George Saunders, one of the greatest modern exemplars of the short story. In his introduction to *A Swim in a Pond in the Rain*, which has been described as 'a literary masterclass on what makes great short stories work', Saunders writes: 'Years ago, on the phone with Bill Buford, then fiction editor of the *New Yorker*, enduring a series of painful edits, feeling a bit insecure, I went fishing for a compliment. "But what do you *like* about the story?" I whined. There was a long pause at the other end. And Bill said this: "Well, I read a line. And I like it...enough to read the next."

'And that was it: his entire short story aesthetic and presumably that of the magazine. And it's perfect. A story is a linear-temporal phenomenon. It proceeds, and charms us (or doesn't), a line at a time. We have to keep being pulled into a story in order for it to do anything to us.' In my many years as a publisher I have never come across a simpler and more effective description of the form. And it tells us exactly why Ruskin's stories are so brilliant. One perfect line is followed by the next and the next and before you know it you are completely engrossed in the tale that's being told.

I have had the good fortune of having published Ruskin for about forty years and have seen him at various stages of his career. In all that time, the excellence of his fiction has never dipped, a trait that is only true of writers who are a class apart. This collection contains the best of his recent fiction. All the stories have been written over the past ten years or so and show that the creative flame that burns within Ruskin has not dimmed in the least. Hilarious stories about crooks and conmen rub shoulders with horror stories, murder mysteries, and diaphanous literary marvels, giving us, once more, a feast of fiction from a literary master.

The long river of Ruskin's short fiction first began over fifty years ago. First seeing the light of day in newspapers and magazines, and then acquiring more permanent form in books—literally, dozens of them—the river has kept rolling on, a pool here, a rill there, an eddy from time to time, but no matter the strength of the current, the water is always clear, always refreshing, with new tributaries constantly freshening the flow of fiction. Drink deep.

DD
New Delhi
April 2022

SONG OF THE FOREST

We think of forests as places of solitude and silence, except when tigers roar and elephants trumpet; but there are always sounds, more subtle than these, that come to the notice of the sensitive wanderer.

Many years ago I lived in a small cottage on the edge of the forest, on the outskirts of the hill station of Mussoorie. A steep and narrow footpath led down through oaks and maples to the red-roofed house that was to be my home for several years.

It was early summer, and when I opened the windows I was assailed by the strident chorus of hundreds of cicadas informing me, and anyone who cared to listen, that it would be raining before long. The cicadas make their shrill music by scraping their legs against their quivering bodies. It's hard to find them—they merge with the trunks of the trees they inhabit—but they are there all summer, constantly reminding you of their presence.

I was a great walker in those days, and my walks took me down to the stream at the bottom of the hill. It made its own sounds, as it tumbled over the rocks and pebbles rendered smooth by hundred of years of the passage of running water. Often, a forktail could be seen hopping from one rock to another. It was a silent bird, pursuing dragonflies that hovered over the sunlit stream. Not so silent were the magpies, who gossiped in the overhanging branches of willows, water-wood, and walnut. And in the brambles, the wild raspberry and blackberry bushes, small birds—wagtails and finches—made merry.

On a knoll above the stream was a lone pine tree, and sometimes I would recline beneath it, notebook and ball-point pen at hand, and write a poem or part of a story or a 'remembrance of things past'. But I was no Proust. My mentors were Thoreau and Richard Jefferies. *Walden* and *The Story of My Heart* were often my companions.

To write a poem upon a grassy knoll, with a zephyr, a gentle breeze, playing in the branches of pine, is to live the poem even as you write it. And today, looking back over the years, I can hear the breeze and feel it, and listen to the sound of the stream, the song of the forest, and it is the poem of all my days.

ς

And sometimes, late in the evening, as the full moon rose over the summit of Landour, silhouetting the deodars, I would go out for one of my nocturnal walks, and then the sounds would be more muted, more secretive. An owl talking to himself in the depths of an old oak tree.

A nightjar making an occasional comment, like a tap on a table.... A barking deer. Something urgent, frantic about its call tonight. It is on the run from a predator.

Presently I hear the sawing cough of a leopard. It is not an animal that roars in order to intimidate. Like most cats, big or small, it is a silent pursuer. Even so, that cough is a distinctive one.

My balcony light is on. From my window I can see the garden at the rear of the cottage. No porcupines about; my dahlia bulbs are safe. But darting into the garden is the terrified barking deer. It runs here and there, looking for a hiding place, then dashes into my woodshed and stands trembling behind a stack of firewood. Will it be safe there?

Leopards were made to hunt and devour their prey; but tonight I am on the side of the helpless deer. I have no gun, being averse to such abominations. But I can make enough noise to scare the leopard away. There are some firecrackers in a cupboard. I light a string of crackers and toss them into the garden. They rattle away like a machine gun, shattering the silence of the forest.

Has the leopard gone away? I have no idea. But presently that barking deer slips out of its place of refuge and darts into a thicket of dog roses. There are no sounds of a struggle. Perhaps it is safe for the night; for this one night, anyway.

ᶜᵖ

I have been in the cottage for three or four years when one day a predator far more dangerous than the leopard arrives on the scene. It is the P. W. D.'s road-building crew, and they have the authority to build a road right through the front garden, in order to link up with another more important road further along the mountains. They have come equipped with explosives, bulldozers, and an army of road workers. I have to move. And so must some of the forest. Oaks, walnuts, pines, maples, all fall to the axe and the electric saw. The birds go elsewhere. Small animals migrate. Even the porcupines abandon the garden, for the dahlias and gladioli have vanished.

I move higher up the mountain. More roads. You can't escape them. I find a small apartment, part of a larger building overlooking the main road, the road to the summit, Lal Tibba. There's plenty of forest up there, but here it's all road, with scores, nay, hundreds of cars from Delhi, Haryana, and Punjab labouring up the hill, honking and tooting, all in a hurry to get a view of the eternal snows. They won't see much unless they get up very early. By noon, cloud and mist have obscured the higher ranges. I hear a tourist from Punjab complaining to his guide: 'You brought us all the way up here, and what did we see? A kabristan, a cemetery!' He was referring to the old Landour cemetery on the north face of the mountain. It has the best view of the snows. But only the old caretaker enjoys the view. The occupants of the graves are still sleeping.

∽

At night the visitors and the cars have gone, the road below is silent except for a dog howling at the moon. It's a warm night and my window is open. The lights are out. Presently a firefly, a jugnu, floats into my bedroom on the night breeze. It moves around, lighting up little spaces. I haven't seen a firefly since I left the old cottage. It's like a visit from an old friend; a tiny star come down to see me in the still of the night.

I feel as though it's summoning me back to my old haunts.

I am too old now to walk to the singing forest, but I will pay homage to it in my own way, with these—my written words. And, in the meantime, keep coming little firefly!

MIRACLE AT HAPPY BAZAAR

It was called 'Happy' Bus Stop because a local boy called 'Happy', happily drunk, had got into the driver's seat of the local bus and driven it over the edge of the cliff, onto the rocks some seventy feet below the road. Fortunately, the bus had been empty at the time, and only Happy and the vehicle had perished.

When I was a boy, the old road to Tehri had been little more than a footpath, and you walked from one village to the next. If you were in a hurry you could take a ride on a mule—mules could navigate the narrowest of tracks—and reach your destination with a very sore bottom. It was wiser to walk.

Then, in mid-1962–63, after the Chinese incursions, there was a flurry of road-building in the hills, and the old footpaths and mule tracks were turned into motorways. A bus stop came up just outside the Landour boundary, and by 1970 there were buses to Chamba and beyond.

Where there is a bus stop you will find a tea shop, and if the tea shop prospers it will be followed by another tea shop. Then there has to be a vegetable stand, because at the last moment bus passengers will remember to buy vegetables to take home. Sometimes they will fetch seasonal vegetables from their own villages to sell in the Landour market—cucumbers and beans during the monsoon rains, pumpkins and maize a little later. The vegetable stalls near the bus stop and in the town will have fruit and vegetables from all over the country—coconuts and pomegranates, pineapples and custard apples.

As the bus stop grew bigger, and the number of buses increased, the shops prospered. One tea shop specialized in pakoras, the other in samosas; the competition remained friendly.

Soon, a little chemist's shop was opened. After all, there was a hospital nearby, and sometimes the patients, or their relatives, required medicines that were not available from the hospital's small pharmacy. Sick and injured people from the surrounding villages would use the buses to come to the hospital. The town had one ambulance and this was usually engaged in bringing townspeople to the emergency ward. The ambulance had a loud, piercing siren, and people living along the main road would be woken up in the middle of the night, or in the early hours before daybreak, by the wail of the ambulance.

Early morning, the first bus left for Chamba. Late evening, the last bus arrived at 'Happy' Bus Stop. Gradually, the owners of the shops expanded their shacks into brick houses. They teetered over the side of the road, packed together like an upside-down Potala Palace.

By the 1990s there were at least ten shops (and residences) near the bus stop, and people began calling it a market. They had forgotten who 'Happy' was, but they called it the Happy Bazaar.

And presently a 'wine' shop opened, to relieve the thirst of bus drivers, passengers, shopkeepers, hospital patients, and their relatives, and anyone who cared to stroll down Happy Bazaar. It wasn't strictly a wine shop, merely an outlet for country liquor. If you wanted 'foreign liquor' (i.e. whisky or rum) you had to go to the 'English Wine Shop' in town, where you could get Indian-made foreign liquor.

The country liquor was strong stuff and sometimes fights broke out and accidents took place. An inebriated bus driver tried to take a shortcut to Chamba by avoiding the road altogether, with the result that both he and many of his passengers took a shortcut into their next incarnations.

Fortunately, there was a police outpost not too far away, and things did not get out of hand too often.

All went well for several years, and the population of Happy Bus Stop and Happy Bazaar grew and prospered. They did not pay much attention to the new road that was being built, a bypass that would provide an alternative route into the mountains. And one day, amidst much fanfare, a minister from the state's capital arrived and opened a new bus stop, a couple of miles from Happy Bazaar, and flagged off a brand new bus to Chamba and beyond.

The Happy Bus Stop continued to function—but not for long. The claims of the new bus stop were considered to be much stronger, and it had political backing, which made all the difference. One by one the buses and their crew moved on to the new site. There was a marked decline in the number of people who used the little marketplace. Fruit and vegetables piled up, and the owner of the vegetable stall was kept busy all day, dousing his wares with cold water in order to keep them fresh. One of the tea shops closed down, the owner renting premises at the new site. I remained loyal to the remaining tea shop, as I preferred pakoras to samosas, and, besides, my home was close by.

I sat alone in the tea shop, keeping the owner company.

'Well, at least the mules are back,' said Melaram abruptly. He was always the optimist.

'This was always their road,' I said. 'They resent the cars and buses.'

The muleteers and local villagers helped to make up the loss of business, but it wasn't quite the same; they did not have much money to spend. Occasionally, Melaram would provide tea and pakoras to the relatives of patients who were in the hospital, and this kept him going. And the chemist's shop remained in business, and so did old Abdul the Bulbul (as he was called by the children) who made mattresses and razais for the hospital and local residents. But most of the time Happy Bazaar wore a forlorn look.

And then one day, as I was sitting in the tea shop, contemplating a dish of pakoras, a dapper-looking gentleman walked in and ordered a cup of tea. Melaram and I took notice. It was some time since a stranger had walked into the shop.

Over a glass of hot tea he seemed inclined to talk, although when we asked him where he came from, he was rather vague and mentioned some town in Kyrgyzstan or Tajikistan, I'm not sure which, and told us his name was Dr Cosmo.

'You can call me Cosmos if you like,' he said with a brilliant smile. 'In reality I belong to the world. To the universe.'

'And what kind of doctor are you?' asked Melaram. 'Can you cure my rheumatism?'

'Of course,' said the stranger. 'But to tell the truth, I'm looking for a quiet place where I can rest from my labours. All this healing can be very taxing. But come closer. Tell me where it hurts. Is there a swelling?'

'In my wrist,' said Melaram. 'And in my elbow. It's worse at night. The pain prevents me from sleeping.'

'Give me your hand.'

Melaram presented his hand, and the stranger took it and held it for some time.

'Do you feel anything?' he asked.

'No.'

The stranger held it a little longer—long enough for me to finish my tea and pakoras.

'I feel a tingling,' said Melaram.

'Good. That's the energy from my body passing into you. It's called cosmic energy. It comes from the sun. It's absorbed by me, and I pass it on to you. You will sleep well tonight. There will be no pain. Now tell me where I can find a place to stay. I like the look of this place. It's restful, at peace with itself.'

'It's restful because most of the people have gone away,' said Melaram. 'This used to be a busy bus stop. But the bus stop was moved closer to the town, and most of our business has gone with it. There's no hotel here. But I have a spare room behind the shop. It used to be occupied by a tailor, but he's moved on too. It's a very simple room—too simple for you, perhaps.'

'The simpler the better,' said Dr Cosmo. 'A good bed, a clean bathroom—and breakfast, perhaps?'

'His parathas are very good,' I chimed in.

'Then lead on, my friend. Show me your honeymoon suite.'

And the next day the good doctor—healer would be a better word—moved in, accompanied by just a few worldly possessions, or rather necessities, and absolutely no medicines or any indication that he was a conventional doctor.

But he liked being called 'doctor', and to one and all he would be known as 'Dr Cosmos'.

11

Melaram's rheumatic pains disappeared overnight, and he lost no time in telling his friends and neighbours of his tenant's healing powers. And it didn't take long for others with chronic disabilities to turn up at the tea shop seeking similar treatment.

Dr Cosmos obliged everyone. He laid his hands on you—on head or heart or back or foot or wherever the patient felt pain or weakness—and then gave the sufferer a few words of encouragement and sent him on his way. Soon people reported that they felt better; some even claimed to be cured. Cripples stood straight and walked with a spring in their step. Old women abandoned their wheelchairs and climbed steep hillsides on foot.

Word of the miraculous healings spread beyond the hill station, and soon the sick and weary from other parts of the land were making their way to Happy Bazaar in search of cures.

Dr Cosmos did not claim to be a faith healer or a dispenser of miracles. It had nothing to do with religion, he said. It was all cosmic energy. It passed through him and into the sufferer, and behold, the pains, the weariness, the ailments disappeared.

'You can try doing it yourself,' he said.

Well, I did try it, but without any success. I tried to cure an old woman's toothache by placing my hand on her cheek, and she brushed it away, saying I was a cheeky fellow and a fraud.

But no one accused Dr Cosmos of being a fraud. Not everyone got better or was returned to normal, but a good many did seem to benefit from his doses of cosmic energy, and he was in great demand. Before long he needed a couple of helpers, and a large room, and these were provided by the bazaar people. They also persuaded him to accept a small fee from his patients to pay for his board and lodging.

A guest house came up to accommodate patients from other towns. It was built where the old bus stop had stood. Nearby hotels and hostelries were reported to be full, even off season. Cars rolled up with rich sufferers, ready to part with large sums of money if they could be cured of chronic ailments, cancer or diabetes or old injuries. And Dr Cosmos treated them too but did not take any 'fees'.

Then some medical men persuaded him to come to Delhi to demonstrate his 'powers', to lecture them on cosmic energy. He made several trips to the capital. He was becoming famous. But every time he returned from Delhi he looked a little thinner, a little more frail, a bit like some of his patients. It was clear that the capital's air or water or atmosphere did not agree with him. He had become accustomed to the good, clean air of the hills.

'Up here, the cosmic energy flows without hindrance,' he claimed.

'Then stay up here,' said Melaram. 'You can't cure all of Delhi of their ailments. I don't go there myself. They should move the capital elsewhere!'

'Someone tried that long ago,' I said. 'They moved

to Daulatabad. But it didn't work. I think they missed the dear old Jamuna.'

So Dr Cosmos's trips to Delhi continued, and although his fame grew, his own health deteriorated, so much so that I felt tempted to say, 'Physician, heal thyself.'

When I heard that he had been admitted to one of the capital's premier hospitals, with an 'unknown' and unspecified complaint, I went down to see him, accompanied by Melaram.

Lying there in his hospital bed, he looked desiccated, devoid of life's juices. This was not the Dr Cosmos we knew. He was barely recognizable. His cheeks were sunken, his teeth missing, his hair falling out. But he recognized us, and raised his hand in a feeble greeting.

'What happened to you?' I asked.

He shook his head, whispered: 'I took on too much. Now I have all the diseases in the world. It's a wonderful thing, in a way. Absorbing their fits and fevers, giving them energy in return.'

'Cosmic energy,' I said. 'You should have kept some for yourself.'

He nodded. 'I will recover. I will regain my strength as soon as I am back in the mountains.'

But he did not return to the mountains. Melaram and I had to return without him. He was too far gone. And a week later we heard that he had joined the cosmos. Some of his relatives turned up and buried him in a corner of a Delhi cemetery; there is no tombstone to mark the place, no record of his fleeting presence on planet earth. No cause of death had been given; but the medical report did mention that traces of strontium had been found in his blood. How did this obscure metallic element get into his system? Had it something to do with the cosmic energy he radiated? We shall never know. There will always be mysteries.

∽

It was thought that the passing of Dr Cosmos would affect the popularity of Happy Bazaar as a destination for tourists. But this did not happen. Curious visitors continued to come our way, many of them eager to see the humble room in which the healer had first seen his patients and sent them happily on their way, bursting with cosmic energy. Some felt that by touching his desk or chair or bed they would obtain relief from their various ailments. And perhaps they did. For thought is a wonderful thing, and mind can prevail over matter.

Happy Bazaar continued to prosper, and so did Melaram, for he owned the premises, and although he did not charge an entry fee, visitors would spend some time in his tea shop, sampling his tea and pakoras. No one made better pakoras.

I was present when a local guide brought a group of tourists into the shop, and expounded on the history of Happy Bazaar, telling them how it had gained its reputation for happiness because of the miracles performed by the now legendary doctor.

I tried to interrupt and tell them that the bazaar had in fact got its name from the delinquent youth 'Happy' who had driven a bus over a nearby cliff. But no one was listening to me.

RHODODENDRONS IN THE MIST

Blood-red, the fallen blossoms lay on the snow, even more striking when laid bare. On the trees they blended with the foliage. On the ground, on those patches of recent snow, they seemed to be bleeding.

It had been a harsh winter in the hills, and it was still snowing at the end of March. But this was flowering time for the rhododendron trees, and they blossomed in sun, snow, or pelting rain. By mid-afternoon the hill station was shrouded in a heavy mist, and the trees stood out like ghostly sentinels.

The hill station wasn't Simla, where I had gone to school, or Mussoorie, where I was to settle later on. It was Dalhousie, a neglected and almost forgotten hill station in the western Himalaya. But Dalhousie had the best rhododendron trees, and they grew all over the mountain, showing off before the colourless oaks and drooping pines.

But I wasn't in Dalhousie for the rhododendrons. It was 1959, and the Dalai Lama had just fled from Tibet, seeking sanctuary in India. Thousands of his followers and fellow-Tibetans had fled with him, and these refugees had to be settled somewhere. Dalhousie, with its many empty houses, was ideal for this purpose, and a carpet-weaving centre had been set up on one of the estates. The Tibetans made beautiful rugs and carpets. I know nothing about carpet-weaving, but I was working for CARE, an American relief organization, and I had been sent to Dalhousie (with the approval of the Government of India) to assess the needs of the refugees.

This is not the story of my tryst with the Tibetans, although I did suffer greatly from drinking large quantities of butter tea, which travels very slowly down the gullet and feels like lead by the time it reaches your stomach. The carpet-weaving centre became a great success, and I went on to work for CARE for several years; but that's another story. Out of one experience came another experience, as often happens during our peregrinations on planet earth, and it was during my stay in Dalhousie that I had a strange and rather unsettling experience.

I was staying at a small hotel which was quite empty as no one visited Dalhousie in those days and certainly not at the end of March. The hill station had been convenient for visitors from Lahore, but Partition had put an end to that.

∽

The hotel had a small garden, bare at this time of the year. But on the second day of my stay, returning from the carpet-weaving centre, I noticed that there was a gardener working on the flower beds, digging around and transplanting some seedlings. He looked up as I passed, and for a moment I thought I knew him. There was something familiar about his features—the slit eyes, the broad, flattened nose, the harelip—yes, the cleft lip was very noticeable—but he wasn't anyone I knew or had known, at least I didn't think so.... He was just a likeness to someone I had seen somehow, somewhere else. It was a bit of a tease.

And it would have remained just that if he hadn't looked up and met my gaze.

A flood of recognition crossed his face. But then he looked away, almost as though he did not want to recognize me; or be recognized.

I passed him. It was curious, but it didn't bother me. We keep bumping into people who look slightly familiar. It is said that everyone has a double somewhere on this planet. I had yet to meet mine—God forbid!—but perhaps I was seeing someone else's double.

I was relaxing in the veranda later that evening, browsing through an old magazine, when the gardener passed me on his way to the garden shed to put away his tools. There was something about his walk that brought back an image from the past. He had a slight limp. And when he looked at me again, his harelip registered itself on my memory. And now I recognized him. And of course he knew me.

I was the man who'd caught him rifling through my

landlady's cupboards and drawers in Dehradun, some three years previously. I had exposed him, reported him, suggested she dismiss him; but the old lady, a widow, had grown quite fond of the youth, and had kept him in her service. He was good at running about and making himself useful, and, in spite of his cleft lip, he was not unattractive.

When I left Dehradun to take up my job in Delhi, I had forgotten the matter, almost forgotten the young man and my landlady; it was another tenant who informed me that the youth—his name was Sohan—had stabbed the old lady and made off with the contents of her jewel case and other valuables. She had died in hospital a few days later.

Sohan hadn't been caught. He had obviously left the town and taken to the hills or a large city. The police had made sporadic attempts to locate him, but as time passed the case lost its urgency. The victim was not a person of importance. The criminal was a stranger, a shadowy figure of no known background.

But here he was three years later, staring me in the face. What was I to do about him? Or what was he to do about me?

༄

After Sohan had gone to his quarters, somewhere behind the hotel, I went in search of the manager. I would tell him what I knew and together we could decide on a course of action. But he had gone to a marriage and would be back late. The hotel was in charge of the cook who, a little drunk, served dinner in a hurry and retired to his quarters. 'Don't you have a night watchman?' I asked him before he took off. 'Yes, of course,' he replied, 'Sohan, the gardener. He's the chowkidar too!'

An early retirement seemed the best thing all round, especially as I had to leave the next day. So I went to my room and made sure all the doors and windows were locked. I pushed the inside bolts all the way. I made sure the antiquated window frames were locked. As I peered out of the window, I noticed that a heavy mist had descended on the hillside. The trees stood out like ghostly apparitions, here and there a rhododendron glowing like the embers of a small fire. Then darkness enveloped the hillside. I felt cold, and wondered how much of it was fear.

I went to the bathroom and bolted the back door. Now no one could get in. Even so, I felt uneasy. Sohan was still a fugitive from the law, I had recognized him, and I was a threat to his freedom. He had killed once— perhaps more than once—and he could kill again.

I read for some time, then put out the light and tried to sleep. From a distance came the strains of music from a wedding band. Someone knocked on the door. I switched on the light and looked at my watch. It was only 10 p.m. Perhaps the manager had returned.

There was another knock, and I went to the door and was about to open it when some childhood words of warning from my grandmother came to mind: 'Never open the door unless you know who's there!'

'Who's there?' I called.

No answer. Just another knock.

'Who's there?' I called again.

There was a cough, a double-rap on the door.

'I'm sleeping,' I said. 'Come in the morning.' And I returned to my bed. The knocking continued but I ignored it, and after some time the person went away.

I slept a little. A couple of hours must have passed when I was woken by further knocking. But it did not come from the door. It was above me, high up on the wall. I'd forgotten there was a skylight.

I switched on the light and looked up. A face was outlined against the glass of the skylight. I could make out the flat rounded face and the harelip. It appeared to be grinning at me—rather like the disembodied head of the Cheshire cat in *Alice in Wonderland*.

The skylight was very small and I knew he couldn't crawl through the opening. But he could show me a knife—and that was what he did. It was a small clasp knife and he held it between his teeth as he peered down at me. I felt very vulnerable on the bed. So I switched off the light and moved to an old sofa at the far end of the room, where I couldn't be seen. There didn't seem to be any point in shouting for help. So I just sat there, waiting.... And presumably, without a sound, he slipped away, and I remained on the sofa until the first glimmer of dawn penetrated the drawn window curtains.

୬

The manager was apologetic. 'You should have rung the bell,' he said, 'someone would have come.'

'The bell doesn't work. And someone did come...'

'I'm sorry, I'm sorry. The fellow's a villain, no doubt about it. And he's missing this morning. Your presence here must have frightened him off. So he's wanted for theft and murder. Well, we shall inform the police. Perhaps they can pick him up before he leaves the town.'

And we did inform the police. But Sohan had already taken off. The milkman had seen him boarding the early morning bus to Pathankot.

Pathankot was a busy little town on the plain below Dehradun. From there one road goes to Jammu, another to Dharamsala, a narrow-gauge railway to Kangra, and the main railway to Amritsar or Delhi. Sohan could have taken any of those routes. And no one was going to go looking for him. A police alert would be put out—a mere formality. He wasn't on their list of current criminals.

That afternoon I took a taxi to Pathankot and whiled away the evening at the railway station. My train, an overnight express to Delhi, left at 8 p.m. There was no rush at that time of the year. I had a first-class compartment to myself.

In those days our trains were somewhat different from what they are today. A first, second, or third class compartment was usually a single carriage, or bogey. We did not have corridor trains. Bogeys were connected by steel couplings, otherwise you were not connected in any way to the other compartments. But there was an emergency cord above the upper berths, and if you pulled it, the train might stop. There were always troublemakers on the trains, just as there are today, and sometimes the chain was pulled out of mischief. As a result it was often ignored.

As the train began moving out of the station I went to all the windows and made sure that they were fastened. Then I bolted the carriage door. I was becoming adept at bolting doors and windows. Sohan was probably hiding out in some distant town or village, but I wasn't taking any chances.

The train gathered speed. The lights of Pathankot receded as we plunged into a dark and moonless night. I had a pillow and a blanket with me, and I stretched out on one of the bunks and tried to think about pleasant things such as scarlet geraniums, fragrant sweet peas, and the beautiful Nimmi, star of the silver screen; but instead I kept seeing the grinning face of a young man with a harelip. All the same, I drifted into sleep. The rocking movement of the carriage, the rhythm of the wheels on the rails, have always had a soothing effect on my nerves. I sleep well in trains and rocking chairs.

But not that night.

I woke to the sound of that familiar tapping; not at the door, but on the window glass not far from my head. The insistent tapping of someone who wanted to get in.

It was common enough for ticketless travellers to

hang on to the carriage of a moving train, in the hope that someone would let them in. But they usually chose the crowded second or third-class compartments; a first-class traveller, often alone, was unlikely to let in a stranger who might well turn out to be a train robber.

I raised my head from my pillow, and there he was, clinging to the fast-moving train, his face pressed to the glass, his harelip revealing part of a broken tooth.... I pulled down the shutters, blotting out his face. But, agile as a cat, he moved to the next window, the sneer still on his face. I pulled down that shutter too.

I pulled down all the shutters on his side of the carriage. He couldn't get in, bodily. But mentally, he was all over me.

Mind over matter. Well, I could apply my mind too. I shut my eyes and willed my tormentor to fall off the train!

No one fell off the train (at least no one was reported to have done so), but presently we slowed to a gradual stop and, when I pulled up the shutters of the window, I saw that we were at a station. Jalandhar, I think. The platform was brightly lit and there was no sign of Sohan. He must have jumped off the train as it slowed down. It was about one in the morning. A vendor brought me a welcome glass of hot tea, and life returned to normal.

I did not see Sohan in the years that followed. Or rather, I saw many Sohans. For two or three years I was pursued by my 'familiar'. Wherever I went—and my work took me to different parts of the country—I found myself encountering young men with harelips and a menacing look. Pure imagination, of course. He had every reason to stay as far from me as possible.

Gradually, the 'sightings' died down. Young men with harelips became extremely rare. Perhaps they were all going in for corrective surgery.

The years passed, and I had forgotten my familiar. I had given up my job in Delhi and moved to the hills. I was a moderately successful writer, and a familiar figure on Mussoorie's Mall Road. Sometimes other writers came to see me, in my cottage under the deodars. One of them invited me to have dinner with him at the old Regal hotel, where he was staying. Before dinner, he took me to the bar for a drink.

'What will you have, whisky or vodka?'

No one seemed to drink anything else. I asked for some dark rum, and the barman went off in search of a bottle. When he returned and began pouring my drink, I noticed something slightly familiar about his features, his stance. He was almost bald, and he had a grey, drooping moustache which concealed most of his upper lip. He glanced at me and our eyes met. There was no sign of recognition. He smiled politely as he poured my drink. No, it definitely wasn't Sohan. He was too refined, for one thing. And he went about his duties without another glance in my direction.

Dinner over, I thanked my writer friend for his hospitality, and took the long walk home to my cottage. It was a dark, moonless night. No one followed me, no one came tapping on my bedroom window.

∽

Mussoorie had its charms. In my mind, every hill station is symbolized by a particular tree, even if it's not the dominant one. Dalhousie has its rhododendrons, Simla its deodars, Kasauli its pines, and Mussoorie its horse chestnuts. The monkeys would do their best to destroy the chestnuts, but I would collect those that were whole and plant them in people's gardens, whether they wanted them or not. The horse chestnut is a lovely tree to look at, even if you can't do anything with it!

My walks took me to the Regal from time to time, and occasionally I would relax in the bar, chatting to an old resident or a casual visitor, while the barman poured me a rum and soda. He never looked twice at me. And I never saw him outside that barroom. He appeared to be as much of a fixture as the moth-eaten antler-head on the wall, only he wasn't quite as moth-eaten.

'Efficient chap,' said Colonel Bhushan indicating the barman. 'And a great favourite with his mistress.'

'You mean the owner of this place?' I had only a vague idea of who owned what in the town. And in some cases the ownership was rather vague. But in the case of the Regal—Mrs Kapoor, a wealthy widow in her fifties, was very much in charge, all too visible an owner; well fleshed-out, ample-bosomed, with arms like rolling pins. Her staff trembled at her approach; but not, it seemed, the bartender, who led a charmed life, incapable of doing any wrong.

The lights went out, as they frequently do in this technological age, and the barman brought over our next round of drinks by candlelight.

By the light of a candle I caught a glimpse of the barman's features as he hovered over me. There was only the hint of a harelip, and the candle lit up his slanting eyes and prominent cheekbones. This was the only time I had a really close look at him.

ς

A week later I met Colonel Bhushan on the Mall. This was where all the gossip took place.

'Have you heard what happened last night at the Regal?' He wasted no time in getting to the news of the day.

A twinge of fear, of anticipation, ran through me. 'Nothing too terrible, I hope?'

'That barman chap—always thought he was a bit too smooth—stabbed the old lady, stabbed her two or three times, then plundered her room and made off with jewellery worth lakhs—as well as all the cash he could find!'

'How's the lady?'

'She'll survive. Tough old buffalo. But the rascal got away. By now he must be in Sirmur, or even across the Nepal border. Probably belongs to some criminal tribe.'

Yes, I thought, possibly a descendant of one of those robber gangs who harassed pilgrims on their way to the sacred shrines, or plundered traders from Tibet, or caravans to Samarkand.... To rob and plunder still runs in the blood of the most harmless looking people.

So the barman at the Regal was the same man I'd known in Dehradun and then encountered in Dalhousie. The passing of time had altered his features but not his way of life. By now he would probably be far from Mussoorie. But I had a feeling I'd see him again—if not here, then somewhere else. Each one of us had a 'familiar'—a presence we would rather do without—an unwelcome and menacing guest—and for me it is Sohan.

Where does he come from, where does he go? I doubt if I shall ever know.

But I have a feeling he'll turn up again one of these days. And then?

A MAN CALLED BRAIN

Did Frank Brain possess any redeeming qualities? If so, they were hard to detect. If ever there was a man totally immersed in himself, and in his own sensual pleasures, it was Brain. He had a way with women—spent money on them, seduced them, discarded them—but he had no real friends, just a few layabouts who drank his whisky and listened admiringly to his bragging. And he never stopped bragging.

He bragged about the money he made; he bragged about the influence he had in political circles; he bragged about the socialite women he'd seduced, and the children he had supposedly fathered—although no one had seen any dependants or any indication that he supported them.

Frank Brain supported no one but himself.

And I hated him!

I hated him right from the start—from the time he gave me a bar of chocolate and told me to go out and play in the garden as he had some important business to discuss with my mother. Seven-year-olds are not so easily fooled. I took a round of the garden, ate some of the chocolate, then crept up to the sitting room window and peered through the glass. Frank Brain had an arm around my mother, and his fat lips pressed against her ear—a business conversation, no doubt.

I rapped loudly on the windowpane, then took off and hid in the shrubbery. The front door opened, and Frank Brain stepped out on the veranda, cursing loudly. A cat was sleeping on the doormat. He kicked it away, then drew back and closed the door. I waited a few minutes, then threw a pebble at the front door. Out came Brain again, using all the foul language that made up most of his limited vocabulary. The cat streaked across the lawn, in reach of sanctuary.

Presently Frank Brain got into his car and drove away. It was a World War II Packard, big and showy like its owner, but heavy on petrol.

Frank Brain was a frequent visitor to the house in Dehra, where my mother and I were staying while my father was on active R. A. F. duty, being moved around from Delhi to Karachi to Calcutta to Ceylon.

'Mum, why does Mr Brain keep coming to see us?' I asked one day.

'Why, don't you like him?'

'No. He's fat and ugly and he doesn't stop smoking those smelly cigars.'

'He's been very helpful. And he keeps bringing you presents.'

'I don't want them. When will Daddy come home?'

'When the war's over, I suppose. He may be in Delhi

next month. Frank has offered to drive us to Delhi. Won't that be nice?'

'Can't we go on our own? There's a train to Delhi, isn't there?'

'We'll see when the time comes.'

In the meantime, Frank Brain's visits became more frequent. He sold cars on behalf of an American company based in Delhi, but he had a branch office in Dehra and a wife in Clement Town. Brain never invited us to his home, so we never saw the wife, but my mother said she ran a school of her own. And I would soon be sent to a boarding school in the hills, she told me.

5

The journey to Delhi was a memorable one—one of my earliest memories, in fact—and seventy-five years later I can still recall that drive through the extensive forests of the Doon, through the pass in the Shivalik range, and along the banks of the Ganges canal. Mr Brain at the wheel of his Packard, full of confidence as usual, talking of tigers he had shot and great people he had met; my mother sitting beside him, smoking her favourite Gold Flakes from a round tin. And there was I in the back seat, looking at the scenery and only half listening to the one-sided conversation.

'Look, there's a spotted deer!' I exclaimed, as we passed a startled cheetal. But Frank Brain did not slow down; he had time only for tigers.

There wasn't much traffic on the roads in those far-off days; mostly bullock carts and pony-drawn ekkas or tongas. Only a few people possessed motorcars.

We stopped at a canal rest house for a late afternoon lunch, and then my mother and Mr Brain decided to spend the night there. It was a quiet place, very restful, with only the chowkidar and a couple of village dogs in attendance. Brain had brought his icebox and whisky along, and as the sun went down the soda water bottles popped and the whisky began to flow.... I wandered off on my own, strolling down the path along the canal bank, watching the water move gently, caressingly, downstream. Tall bushes grew along the banks. Parrots flew out of a mango tree. At the bottom of a flight of steps a dhobi was washing clothes, pounding them against the flat stones in what appeared to be an attempt to tear them to pieces.

When I returned to the rest house it was getting dark. The whisky bottle was half empty.

'Where have you been?' asked my mother.

'Just wandering around.'

'Well, your dinner is ready whenever you want it. And then go to bed early. We'll leave before it gets too hot.'

My bed was placed in the middle of a large hall full of connecting doors. Mr Brain and my mother had the bedroom to themselves. Brain had very thoughtfully given me a comic to read. It was called *The Dandy*, and I finished it in ten minutes.

My mother came in and bolted all the doors and switched off the light.

'It's lonely in here,' I said.

'It's quite safe. The chowkidar sleeps in the veranda. If you need anything, call for me.'

I tried to sleep but I could hear Frank Brain and my mother talking in the next room. Apparently another bottle had been opened.

I called out, and Frank Brain opened the door, his huge frame silhouetted against the bedroom light.

'What is it?' he asked.

'Water,' I said. 'I'm thirsty.'

My mother brought me a glass of water.

'Now go to sleep,' she said.

But how do you force yourself to sleep?

I could hear my mother laughing, Frank Brain singing like a drunken sailor; the chowkidar coughing in the veranda; and jackals howling outside the window.

I called out for my mother.

Frank Brain appeared. 'Why don't you go to sleep?'

'I'm thirsty,' I said, 'More water.'

They brought me more water, an entire jugful.

'Now go to sleep,' said Brain, 'or I'll give you a hiding.'

My temper flared up 'Try giving me a hiding, and I'll *kill* you!'

Frank Brain was shocked into silence. My mother said 'Don't talk like that!' Brain threw up his arms, cursed in Hindustani (English being inadequate), and stomped out of the room.

And finally, helped by a frog croaking in the bathroom, I fell asleep.

∽

I was reunited with my father in Delhi, and was to live with him for a couple of years, in Air Force hutments or rented rooms. He wasn't supposed to have a child with him, but somehow he got away with it on compassionate grounds.

My mother came and went occasionally, and finally my parents were legally separated. When my father was transferred to another outpost, I was finally admitted to a boarding school in the hills.

It was many years before I saw Frank Brain again. My father had died, my mother had married a small-town businessman, and I was working in Delhi for a newspaper. On a visit to my mother's, Frank Brain's name cropped up. A visitor, an old friend of my mother's, turned out to be one of Brain's ex-wives or ex-mistresses. She complained bitterly that he had left her stranded with a growing daughter, vehemently denying that she was his child. Apparently he was now living with a woman he had picked up in a sleazy hotel in the old city.

Always intrigued by someone else's scandals, my mother decided to look him up. For me, he was an unpleasant but distant memory, and I had no wish to see him again; but she phoned him to say she was coming over, and she succeeded in dragging me along.

He was living in a bungalow in a rather nondescript part of West Patel Nagar. It was just off the main road, and a constant stream of traffic thundered past the gate.

Brain had, of course, aged in the twenty years since I had last seen him. His belly sagged over his belt; his chin sagged over his collar; he was almost bald.

But otherwise he was full of his usual bluster and false bonhomie; he hugged my mother, kissed her, shook my hand and ushered me into his large bed-sitting room where his current mistress was reclining against a pile of pillows at the head of a large double bed.

She was a sex worker from a notorious area in the old city. Her name was Khushboo, and she certainly lived up to her name, for the room was filled with the strong fragrance of jasmine, attar of roses, and a host of other perfumes. There was nothing passive about this lady. She appeared to have Frank Brain well under her thumb, or rather under her generous bosom, which was where he spent most of the time. Quite unabashed, she laughed and joked and teased the ageing roué, stroking his wobbly chin and chiding him about his declining sexual powers.

'I have to wait until five in the morning,' she said with a laugh, 'before I can get him to do anything!'

I felt quite embarrassed in this company, but Frank Brain did not seem to mind, and my mother seemed to find it amusing. He was quite smitten with his new companion, and was constantly cuddling her, his hands never still, as they roamed over her sensuous body. He was going to marry her, he proclaimed; but we'd heard that before. Frank Brain's affairs and infatuations had never lasted very long; but he was certainly putty in the hands of this queen of her profession. And she seemed quite fond of him, in a bantering sort of way.

But of course she cleaned him out.

∽

It must have been about a year later, when I was passing that way, I stopped outside the gate of Frank Brain's house, wondering if he still lived there. I had no particular desire to see him again, but I was curious.... The lights were out and the place looked unoccupied. There was a lock on the front door. It looked as though he had gone away.

I was about to walk on when a man appeared at the next-door gate. 'Are you looking for someone?' he asked.

'Mr Brain,' I said. 'Has he gone away?'

'Died last month. I'm the landlord. Are you a relative?'

I was surprised but not shocked. Frank Brain had led a life of self-indulgence.

'Just an acquaintance,' I said, 'How did he die?'

'Must have been a heart attack. He'd been on his own for several months, no one to look after him when he fell ill.'

'What about the lady who was staying with him?'

'Left long ago. Took away all his furniture and

carpets. I suppose he owed her money.'

'Was anyone informed when he died?'

'There was no one to inform. He'd been dead two or three days when we found him. Had to break into the house. Informed the police. They went through his things but couldn't find any addresses or phone numbers. So he was taken to the morgue. Kept there for some time. Unclaimed body.'

'So they had him cremated, I suppose.'

'No. Sent the body to the local medical college. The medical students need bodies for study and dissection. Bodies are in short supply. They take what they can get—usually beggars and vagrants.'

Frank Brain a vagrant! It was an interesting thought. And by becoming a subject for dissection he had perhaps finally contributed something to society. Perhaps an examination of his brain would reveal something that would account for the vagaries of human nature; but I doubted it.

As I walked away from that empty, denuded house, the words of a childhood poem, 'The Miller of Dee', ran through my head:

I care for nobody,
No, not I,
And nobody cares for me.

And that just about summed up Mr Frank Brain.

SHER SINGH AND THE HOT-WATER BOTTLE

It's been many years since Sher Singh, of village Solti, came to my rescue.

At the time I was living right at the top of the Landour hill, in a rented cottage that leaked badly. It was cold that winter and I was short of funds and in need of sustenance. And to make matters worse, our new Prime Minister, a strict moralist who knew what was good for everyone, had imposed prohibition on the country, and I was suffering from the non-availability of Solan No. 1 (a cheap but good whisky) and a certain XXX Rum that had been distilled at Rosa in U. P. since before the 1857 revolt. The distillery had changed hands more than once during the fighting, and both oppressors and oppressed had raided it until it was emptied of its energizing grog. It had recovered from those traumatic events; but now, in more peaceful times, it was to suffer again, along with those, such as this writer, who thirsted after the mellowed and matured juices of our all-purpose sugarcane.

Sher Singh was my milkman. Early every morning he

trudged up the hill from his village, three miles distant, to deliver his milk to two or three homes on the hillside. On the way he watered it a little at a roadside hydrant; but it was good milk, once you had removed some of the grass that floated around in the can.

One morning, when Sher Singh found me sitting in the sun looking rather depressed, he offered condolences, well knowing the reason for my dejection.

'Not to worry, sir,' he said, 'When one door closes, another door opens. Every problem has its solution. In three days' time I will have solved your problem.'

Three dry and thirsty days passed. Sher Singh came and went. On the fourth morning he asked me for my hot-water bottle—one of those rubber bags which keep you warm for half the night, allowing you to freeze during the second half.

Anyway, I gave him my hot-water bottle. His need, I felt sure, was greater than mine.

'Do you have another?' he asked.

This was testing my generosity, but I was in a don't-care-mood, and I said, 'To hell with it,' and gave him the second bottle.

Next morning he turned up with both bottles. They were full of something; certainly not milk.

'Don't you want them?' I asked.

'See if you like my home-made brandy,' he said, and unscrewing one of the bottles, he poured a vile-looking liquid into an empty jug.

'Go on, taste it,' he said.

I did as I was told. It tasted awful—a combination of turnips and castor oil—but it lit a small fire in my stomach, and I came to life immediately.

Sher Singh had created his own still and was busy producing a potent and heady liquor for all his friends—and customers.

The hillside came to life. A somnolent Landour became a merry mountain. Strengthened and uplifted, the more adventurous residents of Landour—missionaries, retired colonels and brigadiers, schoolteachers, shopkeepers, and the odd hippie (left over from the sixties)—found themselves immune to the mists of February and sharp winds of March.

We flung aside restraint. Mischief abounded. A respectable headmistress fell in love with a muleteer, and rode off with him to his village near Harsil. A retired vice admiral drank too much one evening and performed a sailor's jig in the middle of the Upper Mall. A judge had an affair with the dhobi's sister, and the local padre developed acute peritonitis and perished from a burst appendix. Not all was merriment in the spring of 1980.

A posse of policemen was sent down to Solti village to find out what was going on down there. They were not seen for several days. After being entertained by Sher Singh and his friends, they had lost their way coming back, and had emerged near the Yamuna bridge, happy to be alive in spite of severe hangovers.

I spent most of my evening in the company of a famous shikari, who was paying me to write his memoirs.

He made up most of his exploits, but it was fun anyway, and after consuming a hot-water bottle of firewater, we saw pink elephants and purple tigers.

Then suddenly this orgy of wine, women, and song came to an end. Sher Singh's supply system had broken down. Our hot-water bottles were dry and empty.

There was no sign of Sher Singh, either.

I decided to go down to his village. Landour was in suspense.

I was in my forties then, still quite agile on a mountain slope, and it took me a little over an hour to scramble down the steep footpath to Solti village.

I found Sher Singh on his cot, his arm in a sling, his head bandaged, strips of plaster on his hands and feet. He had just been carried home, piggyback on a neighbour's shoulder, from the mission hospital.

'The bear attacked me,' he explained. 'It had been raiding my still every evening, and it was becoming a nuisance—getting drunk and chasing the women as they returned from the fields.'

Armed with a lathi, Sher Singh had attempted to chase away the bear, but it had turned on him, using its claws to good effect before taking off into the forest. Lucky to be alive, Sher Singh would carry the scars for the rest of his life.

I was reluctant to trudge back to Landour on my own. I had no desire to encounter an alcoholic bear on the way. Deprived of Sher Singh's magic potion, it would be in a bad mood. Fortunately, several young men of the village offered to escort me home, and we went uphill in style, making a lot of noise to keep the bear away. One youth beat a drum, another blew a bugle, and a third shouted imprecations against bears in general.

The flow of high-spirited spirits having come to a halt, Landour returned to its sober and sombre self. The headmistress returned from Harsil as though nothing unusual had happened, the retired judge fell out of love with the dhobi's sister, and a new padre moved into the parson's house.

Fortunately for some of us, the government in Delhi changed around that time, and the prohibition law was repealed.

'Foreign liquor' (as made in India) appeared again in the stores, and the vendors of home-made spirits went out of business. My hot-water bottles were put to their legitimate use.

When Sher Singh recovered from his wounds he continued to deliver my milk, and did so for many years, always watering it down a little at the tap near Sisters' Bazaar. Then he grew too old to climb up to Landour, and I grew too old to scramble down to his village. But his grandson now delivers the milk on his way to school, and being a good boy, he doesn't water it down.

The other day he told me that his grandfather was feeling the cold. It has been a harsh winter. So I sent the old man one of my hot-water bottles. And for old times' sake, I filled it with the better part of a bottle of rum.

THE SHADOW ON THE WALL

When I was in my early twenties, a struggling freelance writer, I rented two small rooms above a shop in Dehradun, and settled down to make my fortune as an author. Or so I hoped.

The rooms were without electricity, the landlord (the shop owner) having failed to pay the electricity bills for several years; but this did not bother me. Dehra wasn't too hot in those days, and I had no need of a ceiling fan. And I thought an oil lamp would be sufficient and even quite romantic. Hadn't the great authors of the past penned their masterpieces by the light of a solitary lamp? I could picture Goethe labouring over his *Faust*, Shakespeare over his *Sonnets*, Dostoyevsky over his *Crime and Punishment* (probably in a prison cell), and Emily Brontë composing *Wuthering Heights* by the light of a flickering lamp while a snowstorm raged across the moors that surrounded her father's lonely parsonage.

Many geniuses would have written by lamplight—Premchand in his village, Keats in his attic, poor John Clare in a madhouse.... Well, I was no genius and I had no wish to enter a madhouse, but I liked the idea of writing by lamplight, so I invested in a lamp and a bottle of kerosene, set up the lamp on an old dining table (I took my meals at a dhaba down the road), brought it to a fine glow, and wrote a new story under its benediction.

I don't remember what the story was about, but it wasn't a bad effort, and I sold it to a Sunday magazine.

Every evening, after taking my meal in the dhaba, I would light the lamp, settle down at the table, and toss off a story or an article. I enjoyed the lamplight, even when I wasn't writing. There was something soothing about its soft glow. It threw my shadow on the wall on the other side of the desk; and whenever I got up and paced about the room (as I often do when writing) my shadow would follow, prowling about on the walls of the room, almost as though it were taking on a life of its own.

The shadow was always a little larger than life. The lamp seemed to magnify my image. Probably this had something to do with the glass or the position of the lamp. And late one evening, while I was in the middle of a story, I chanced to look up—and there, beside my shadow on the wall, was another shadow. It was the shadow of someone who was standing behind me.

Someone was in the room, looking over my shoulder, reading what I was writing.

It is always irritating to have someone watching you while you work. Even in an exam hall I could never proceed with my essay or answers if the supervisor was standing over me; I would wait for him to move on, so that I could concentrate properly.

So now, disturbed, I turned around to see who was looking over my shoulder.

There was no one behind me, no one was in the room.

I can't say I was frightened. But I felt extremely uneasy. Had I imagined the shadow on the wall—the shadow of the watcher? I looked again. It was no longer there.

I returned to my writing. But I was uneasy. I couldn't help feeling that I was not alone, that someone was reading my manuscript even as it was being written.

Well, doesn't every writer cherish a reader? Why complain? If there can be ghostwriters, there can be ghost readers.

And when I looked up again the shadow was there, standing beside my own seated shadow, very still, studying the page, my words, my stream of consciousness.

It was the shadow of a woman, of that I was certain. Her hair fell to her shoulders, the outline of her figure was feminine, and she was wearing a gown that trailed behind her. All this the shadow told me; but no more.

I put down my pen, covered my manuscript with a paperweight, put out the lamp, and went to bed. In the dark there are no shadows.

The dark has never really bothered me. With my poor sight I am just as home in the dark as I am in a well-lit room. That's why I like the lamplight. It is not too harsh, too intrusive; and beyond its circle of light, there is darkness, the friendly dark that is home to little bats, timid mice, and shy humans.

But lamps throw shadows. And when I sat down at my desk the following evening, I was expecting the shadow of my solitary reader.

I had written a page or two before I became aware of her presence. I knew she was there without looking up to see if her shadow was there on the wall. The room had become suffused with an unmistakable fragrance—attar of roses! She was speaking to me through the perfumes of her favourite flower.

But I was not to be seduced!

I carried on with my story—'Time Stops at Shamli'—completed a few pages, covered them up, put out the lamp, and went to bed.

My visitor must have been annoyed, because the scent of roses vanished, to be replaced by the strong odour of crushed marigolds. I covered my head with a blanket and shut out all scents and shadows.

Next morning I found the pages of my manuscript scattered about the floor of my room. Perhaps the dawn wind had disturbed them. The window was half open. Could my visitor have disturbed them? She was doing her best to make her presence known.

I started working in the mornings instead of at

night. The lamp would be given a rest except when really needed. Let the shadows rest. Let the phantom lady rest....

She did not like being ignored.

Late one night—it must have been about two in the morning, the witching hour—I was awakened by the most terrible shrieks. The room vibrated with the sounds of a shrieking woman.

Scared out of my wits, I leapt out of bed and lit the lamp, which now stood on the dressing table. The shrieking stopped. And shadows scurried about on the walls.

This happened night after night, for almost a week. Shrieks would wake me in the middle of the night, and would stop only when the lamp was lit. No longer did fragrance fill the air; just the smell of oil and something burning.

I confided in Melaram, the owner of the dhaba where I took my meals. He twirled his luxurious moustache, nodded sagely, and said: 'It seems your landlord kept something from you—the tragedy of the woman who perished in your flat some five or six years ago. They were a childless couple, she and her doctor husband. They quarrelled a lot. One day, when she was in the kitchen preparing their dinner, the petromax stove burst, burning oil fell on her clothes and soon she was covered in flames. She ran on to the balcony, screaming for help, but by the time we could get to her she was in a terrible state.'

'And where was her husband?'

'Out, visiting a patient. He followed us to the hospital, but by then she had gone. In fact, there wasn't much left of her.'

'So it was an accident?'

'The police called it an accident. But there were rumours—there are always rumours in such cases, and when the doctor left town and set up his practice in Delhi, there were more rumours. And then of course he married again....'

'All speculation,' I said, 'But I've had enough of the lady's presence. Her shadow seems real enough—and now those shrieks! I'm moving into the station hotel, and then perhaps you can help me find another flat.'

But I could not move immediately. Two suitcases held all my clothes and personal effects, but I had accumulated a cupboard full of books, and these, along with my notebooks and manuscripts, had to be carefully packed. It meant another night in my haunted rooms.

I went to bed as late as possible. I went to bed in the dark. Well, it wasn't too dark, because a full moon threw its beams across the balcony. But I did not light the lamp; I'd had enough of shadows.

I had asked Melaram's young assistant to bring me a glass of hot tea at daybreak. I slept soundly. There was no shrieking that night. But I was awakened by a push on my left shoulder. And I started up and called out 'What's up? Why so early?' thinking it was the boy with my tea. The moonlight had gone and it was dark everywhere.

I got no answer. Instead I received another push.

This annoyed me and I said, 'Why don't you speak, boy? Is something wrong?'

Still no answer, and as I began to sit up I felt a human hand, warm, plump and soft, slip into mine.

Still thinking it was the boy, I held the hand; but my free hand encountered a wrist and arm, a long sleeveless arm. I felt along the arm, but when I reached the elbow all trace of the arm ceased. I was left holding a disembodied arm!

You can imagine my fright. I dropped the arm, tumbled out of bed, and rushed to the balcony calling for help. Melaram was up by then, and he and his boy came rushing to my aid with torches and an old firearm. But there was no one in the room, no remnants of a burnt or dismembered body. And soon it was daylight.

ى

After a few nights in the station hotel, I found a bright, cheerful flat just behind the Odeon cinema. It had electricity too. Although we were subject to long power cuts, I was no longer dependent on the oil lamp, which I still possessed—just in case I couldn't pay the light bills!

But somehow I missed the gentle glow of my oil lamp. I had a feeling that I wrote better by lamplight than by daylight or the harsh light of electricity. The lamp provided the right kind of atmosphere for my writing; it created the mood I wanted, a touch of mystery, a touch of melancholy, of emotions undefined....

And so one evening I lit the lamp, sat back on an easy chair, and watched the shadows on the wall.

But there were no shadows apart from mine, no one looking over my shoulder. In the words of the old song, it was just 'my echo, my shadow, and me....' And we weren't really company.

I decided to visit a friend at the other end of town. I returned home late. I was too tired to do any work, so I left the lamp burning and went to bed. Outside, on the street, a clock struck twelve.

I was slipping into a dream when I felt that soft hand on my shoulder. Then the other hand touched me. I shivered with fright and apprehension. The hands moved across my chest and arms, there was nothing disembodied about them. I lay perfectly still.

A soft, warm, plump arm brushed against my cheek. I put out my hand to discover, to touch her face. But there was nothing to touch. She was headless!

As I tried to get up, her free arm stretched out, stretched right across the room, and switched off the lamp. I was in bed with a headless woman!

And that's when I woke up. That's when I always wake up. For it's a dream, a nightmare that has pursued me over the years, slowly driving me out of my mind as I try to imagine what the missing head looks like.

BREAKFAST AT BAROG

It's well over seventy years that I actually breakfasted at Barog, that little railway station on the Kalka–Simla line; but last night I dreamt of it—dreamt of the station, the dining room, the hillside, and the long dark Barog tunnel—which meant that it had been present in my subconscious all these years and was now striving to come to the fore and revive a few poignant memories.

Should I go there again? The station is still there, and so is the tunnel. I'm told that the area has been built up over the years, so that it is now almost a mini hill station. That wouldn't surprise me. Our villages have become towns, our towns have become cities, and in a few years' time our country will be one vast megacity with a few parks here and there to remind us that this was once a green planet.

I don't remember any dwellings around Barog, just that one little station and its one little restaurant with a cook and a waiter and its one little stationmaster. No, such a small station couldn't have had someone as important as a stationmaster. Someone quite junior must have been in charge.

Never mind. It was the breakfast that was important. And that I was with my father and on my way to Simla and a boarding school. The boarding school was the least desirable part of the journey. It was almost two years since I had been in a school and I was perfectly happy to continue living in an ideal world where schools need not exist. The breakup of my parents' marriage had resulted in my being withdrawn from a convent school in Mussoorie and taken over by my father who was on active service with the RAF. It was 1942 and World War II was at its peak. Against all regulations he kept me with him, but to do this he had to rent a flat in New Delhi. Most of the day he was at work and I would have the flat to myself, surrounded by books, gramophone records, and stamp albums. Evenings I would help him with his stamp collection, for he was an avid collector. On weekends he would take me to see Delhi's historic monuments; there was no dearth of them. From the stamps I learned geography, from the monuments history, from the books literature. I learnt more in two years at home than I did in a year at school.

But finally he was transferred—first Colombo, then Karachi, then Calcutta—and it was no longer possible for me to share his quarters. I was admitted to Bishop Cotton's in Simla.

We took the railcar from Kalka. It glided over the rails without any of the huffing and puffing of the steam engine that dragged the little narrow gauge train up the steep mountain. I would be travelling in that train in the years to come, but on this, my first to Simla, I was given the luxury of the railcar.

It glided into the Barog station punctually at 10 a.m., in time for breakfast.

The Barog breakfast was already well known and I did full justice to it. I skipped the cornflakes and concentrated on the scrambled eggs and buttered toasts. There was bacon too, and honey and marmalade.

'Tuck in, Ruskin,' said my father, 'School breakfasts won't be half as good.'

He didn't eat much himself. There was a lot on his mind in those days, apart from his work. There was his estranged wife, my mother; my invalid sister, now with his mother in Calcutta; his frequent transfers; his own frequent attacks of malaria; and our future in India, once the War was over—for India's Independence was just around the corner.

'When do we get to Simla?' I asked, quite happy to remain in Barog forever.

'In a little over an hour. But first we go through the longest of all the tunnels on this line. It will take about five minutes. Time for you to make a wish.'

The railcar plunged into the tunnel and we were enveloped in the darkness of the mountain. I held my father's hand. A couple of soldiers sitting behind us broke into a song from an earlier war.

Pack up your troubles in your old kitbag,
And smile, smile, smile!

A glimmer of daylight appeared at the end of the tunnel and then we were out in the sunshine and the pine-scented air.

'Did you make your wish?' asked my father.

I nodded, 'I wished that my mother would come back.'

He was silent for a few moments. 'Do you miss her a lot?'

'I don't miss her,' I said firmly. 'I'm always happy with you. But you miss her all the time. I don't like to see you so sad.'

'I've often asked her to come back,' he said. 'But it's up to her. She wants a different kind of life.'

And that was true. She was still very young—in her late twenties—and she enjoyed parties and dances and a busy social life. My father was in his forties. He liked staying at home, listening to classical music. When he took a holiday, he went in search of rare butterflies. My mother was a butterfly too—pretty, merry, fluttering here and there—but most unwilling to be displayed in a butterfly museum.

I suppose for most of us, big or small, life is just a succession of making mistakes and we spend most of our time trying to rectify them. Marriage was a mistake for both my parents. And I was a product of that mistake!

In the time he had, my father did his best for me. And how proud I was of him when he accompanied me down to my new school! He was wearing his dark blue RAF uniform with its flying officer's stripes, and uniforms, especially officers' uniforms, made a great impression amongst schoolboys in those wartime days. I was received with respect and curiosity. Word went around that my father was a fighter pilot and that he'd shot down dozens of Japanese planes! He was another Biggles, that fictional aviator. Nothing could have been further from reality. My father did not fly at all. He worked for a unit called Codes and Cyphers, helping to create new codes or breaking down enemy codes. It was important work and secret work but there was no glamour about it.

Not that I was averse to the glamour of being Biggles Junior. In my previous school I'd been something of an outsider and the Irish nuns hadn't cared much for a quiet, sensitive boy. Here I was made to feel I belonged and in no time at all I made a number of friends. It was already halfway through the school year but I had no difficulty in catching up with my classmates.

This was 'prep' school—junior school—and certainly more fun than senior school, still a couple of years away, would ever be.... Still, I was always looking forward to the winter break, when I would be with my father again, for at least three months. And there he was, waiting at the Old Delhi railway station, as my train drew alongside the platform. He was still in Delhi, at Air Headquarters, and I made the most of my time with him. Connaught Place was close by, and two or three evenings every week, we would go to the cinema. There were four to choose from—the Regal, the Rivoli, the Odeon, and the Plaza, all very new and smart and showing the latest films from Hollywood. I became a regular film buff. The bookshops were there too, and the record shops, and Wenger's with its confectionery and the Milk Bar with its milkshakes and Kwality with its ice creams. It was hard to believe that there was a world war going on in Europe and Asia and North Africa and the Pacific; or that the Quit India movement was at its height and that my father and I might have to leave the country in the near future. He spoke about it sometimes and of the possibility of my going to a school in England. We did not talk about my mother, but I noticed that he still kept a photograph of her in his desk drawer.

It was back to school in March, when the rhododendrons were in bloom. This time I went up with the school party, in the small train with its steam engine chugging slowly up the steep inclines. The journey took all day. We did stop briefly at Barog, but we were not allowed to get down from the train; one or two boys were certain to be left behind. I looked longingly at the little restaurant on the far side of the platform; but it was already teatime. Breakfast was for the railcar!

The school year rolled on. My father was transferred to Karachi and then to Calcutta. He had grown up in Calcutta and knew the city well. He wrote to me every week and in his last letter he told me what I could look forward to during the winter holidays—the New Market with its bookshops, the botanical gardens with its ancient banyan tree, the zoo, the riverfront, the great maidan where hundreds of people would be taking in the evening air.... I was hoping he would come up to see me during the autumn break, but instead I had news of another kind.

It must be difficult for a young schoolmaster, as yet untouched by tragedy, to tell a ten-year-old that he has just lost his father. Mr Murtough was given this onerous duty. And he did his best, mumbling something ridiculous about God needing my father more than I did and so on and so on....

My friends were more natural in expressing this sympathy—giving me their sweets or chocolates, offering to play games with me, talking to me in the middle of the night when they discovered I wasn't asleep.... For the future did look bleak. I wasn't sure where I would be going next—my Calcutta granny or my Dehra granny, or my mother and stepfather.... I did receive a letter from my mother, telling me that my father had died of the malaria that had plagued him for years; but it was an unemotional letter and it did little to bring me comfort.

But I did go to her when school closed for the winter and I was to spend the next few years in my stepfather's home. But that's another story.

I continued my school in Simla, and every year in March, the small train would take me and my schoolmates up the mountain, through numerous tunnels and winding gradients, forests of pine and deodar, and we always stopped at Barog, before the biggest tunnel of all. But

I never made another wish when passing through that tunnel.

That was over seventy years ago.

Is the railcar still running on that line? And do they still serve breakfast at Barog?

They say you should see Venice before you die. Or better still, Varanasi. But I'll settle for that little station among the pines. And if my father is standing on the platform, waiting for me, ready to take me by the hand, I'll be a small boy again and that railcar will take us to a different destination altogether.

THE OLD SUITCASE

The autobiography of my suitcase is, in many respects, my own autobiography.

I bought it in Jersey, in the Channel Islands, in 1952, and for well over sixty-five years it has given shelter to so many of my personal effects—socks, underwear, shirts, trousers; books, notebooks, pens, paper, passport; and in recent years (when, like its owner, it is showing signs of wear and tear): a receptacle for old manuscripts, photographs, newspaper cuttings, publisher's contracts, and the flotsam of a lifetime of putting pen to paper.

For the last few years the suitcase had lain under my bed, so forgotten that the mice had managed to get in, building a nest from old newspapers; and I was woken one night by the squealing of baby mice—several of them. I was about to evict the family when I remembered the times when I had been evicted from lodgings, so I allowed them a respite of several days—a sort of stay order—before tipping the lot into an empty flowerpot and hoping for the best.

The suitcase was in a sad condition, but I was loath

to throw it away. You don't throw away old friends. Or do you? There are all-weather friends and there are fair-weather friends, and it can take time to tell one from the other. The old suitcase had been with me long enough to be called both friend and philosopher, and so I hung on to it.

∽

It was a very cheap suitcase—the cheapest I could find in that Woolworth's Store in Jersey, when I was eighteen and ready to try my luck in London. I had spent a year in Jersey, living with my aunt's family and working as a junior clerk in the Public Health Department. Late evening I'd sit down at my small portable typewriter (bought with the help of a loan from Mr Bromley, a kind senior clerk) and work on the novel that I was writing—the novel that was to become *The Room on the Roof;* but I was keen to move to London, where there were publishers and writers and bookshops and theatres, and I was saving something out of my weekly wage of £3 in order to make that dream a reality.

I had saved about £12 when a decision to leave was forced upon me as result of a quarrel I had with my uncle, a good man but somewhat set in his way of thinking.

I used to keep a diary at the time, and I'd made the mistake of leaving it on my desk near the typewriter in the attic room where I worked. My uncle, prowling

around while I was out at work, had come across and
read some entries in which I had expressed dissatisfaction
with his narrow-mindedness and extreme political views.
He confronted me with the diary. He accused me of being
an ingrate and a 'nigger lover' (his words) and suggested
that I leave his house.

So, of course, I took up his suggestion, gave a week's
notice to the Public Health Department, and packed my
belongings. Jersey was not for me.

But I needed a suitcase—and a cheap one. The tin
trunk I had brought from India was unsuitable for
travelling about in England, where you had to manage
your own luggage. The suitcase I found was very light—
made of some sort of reinforced hardboard—and I did
not expect it to last very long. But it was big enough for
my few belongings, and it cost £2 and a few shillings.

And so, with my new suitcase in my right hand, and
the typewriter in my left hand, I boarded the ferry for
Southampton, and eight hours later found myself on the
train to London—without a job, without a home to go
to, and with a half-written novel as my only asset.

∽

The gales of Jersey were exchanged for the fog of
London. March is probably the most dismal month in
that hardy city—fog outside, and indoors the smell of
leaking gas. Continuous drizzle. Aspidistras growing in
dark corners of boarding-house entrance halls. The sun

a distant memory. I cursed myself for leaving India.

An old school friend put me up in his small room for almost a month. He loved cooking, and the room was always full of the fragrance of curries and spices. I found a job and a room of my own, and typewriter, suitcase, and I ascended the stairs to a tiny attic room in a boarding house in Glenmore Road.

It was a depressing little room, but I was out most of the day, working in an office in distant Soho, or wandering about looking for cheap cafés, living off beans on toast or 'meat and two veg'—the staple chow in the ABC restaurants. When I had money to spare I went to the cinema. Everyone smoked in those days, and it was difficult to see the screen through the haze of smoke that drifted through the hall.

I left Glenmore Road for Haverstock Hill, my suitcase getting heavier with the few books that I had been acquiring. At night I worked on my novel—the first draft written by hand, the second draft typed out on my little portable.

Diana Athill, a partner in the firm of Andre Deutsch and about fifteen years my senior, befriended me and had me over for dinner on several occasions. She gave me an old raincoat—we were about the same height—and out of gratitude I showed her how to make a curry. I think it was more of a stew than a curry, but we managed to consume it.

Then the three friends—suitcase, typewriter, and budding author—moved to Tooting, in South London.

Why Tooting?

Well, I'd fallen in love with this wonderful girl from Vietnam. She was a student and her name was Vu-Phuong, meaning 'like the wind', and true enough, she came and went like the wind.

She was sweet company, and for several weeks we spent a lot of time together—strolling in Kensington Gardens, wandering through the hothouses in Kew, even going to the opera. It was my suggestion that we go to the opera. The cheaper seats were right at the back of the huge opera house, and we couldn't hear much of the singing, not even the rollicking Toreador song (it was *Carmen*)—it was much better on gramophone records!

On a rainy day in June we joined the crowds on the streets, watching Queen Elizabeth's coach pass by in all its splendour. Vu had a pretty umbrella and I had Diana Athill's raincoat, so we did not mind the rain.

And then, unaccountably, Vu stopped seeing me. She even changed her lodgings without giving me her new address. I tried to trace her, but without any success. Then I received a note from her saying she was returning to her home in Hanoi. The Vietnam War was at its height, and Hanoi was part of Communist-held territory. It was possible that she was under pressure to avoid contact with 'Westerners'. I was no Westerner, but how were her political bosses to know that? Heartbroken, I left Tooting—how I hated Tooting!—and returned to the more familiar streets of Belsize Park.

I told Diana of my unhappy plight—I would often

confide in her—and to cheer me up she took me to St Paul's Cathedral to hear Yehudi Menuhin, the great violinist, give a recital. It was a moving experience, and for once I felt grateful to London for giving me the opportunity to hear great music.

᠅

Another kind of music assailed me when I made friends with a bunch of West Indians, newly arrived in England. They invited me to a calypso party in a flat in Brixton (right next to the prison), and the dancing and revelry continued till dawn. Unthinking, I invited them to hold their next party in my bedsitter (now a fairly spacious one) in Belsize Park. The party was a great success, the building shuddered to its foundations as the rum flowed and the dancing grew frenetic, and the next day my landlord gave me twenty-four-hours' notice to leave the premises.

I lugged my suitcase and typewriter down the road to Swiss Cottage, where a kindly Jewish landlady (my third Jewish landlady) took me in and gave me a pleasant room with a large window which let in the sunlight on those few occasions when the sun came out. She even gave me a good breakfast. But she warned me against having parties in the room. And no lady visitors. And no pin-ups on the walls. Down came Eartha Kitt.

I was quite happy in Swiss Cottage, but after nearly four years away from India I felt it was time to go home.

'No job for you here,' my mother had warned me. 'And you won't make any money from writing. Better stay in England.'

But I was not to be put off. Home is where the heart is, and my heart was still in the foothills of Dehra.

After much dithering, Diana and Andre Deutsch gave me a cheque for £50 as an advance against my novel, which had finally been accepted. This was the standard advance in those days. Publication was still a year off, but I did not feel like hanging around in London any longer. The fare to Bombay—by the cheapest passenger liner, the M. S. *Batory*, a Polish ship—was just under £40. I bought a ticket, gave a week's notice to my employer, thanked Diana for her many kindnesses, and bought a second suitcase.

This new suitcase cost more than the old one, and was quite flashy, but it was not to last as long. The cheap hardboard suitcase had accompanied me all over London, from one boarding house to another, and had attached itself to me like an unwanted stray, knowing no one else would keep it.

∽

The M. S. *Batory* had a reputation for being unlucky, and even before it sailed half the crew had sought political asylum in the UK. But it had a good bar, serving Polish vodka, and only one passenger fell overboard in the course of the voyage.

At Gibraltar I went ashore and bought several bottles of perfume from an Indian trader. These, I thought, would make suitable presents for friends and family. At Port Said I went ashore and had my pocket picked; fortunately I'd kept most of my money in the old suitcase. At Aden I went ashore and did nothing; there was nothing to do and nothing to see. At Bombay I stepped ashore with my suitcases and was met by a couple of young customs officials and told to open them. I did so, and they took away all my bottles of perfume. Contraband, they said.

Happy homecoming!

'What will they do with it?' I asked a fellow passenger.

'Give it all to their girlfriends this evening,' he said knowingly.

At least they left my typewriter alone. And suitcases, typewriter, and I arrived in Dehradun without further mishap. I had no presents for anyone, but I was welcomed back anyway.

∽

And so began three years of freelancing, bombarding every magazine and newspaper in the land with stories, articles, and anything they would publish and pay for! The little typewriter broke down from all the strain, the letter 'b' breaking off; being irreplaceable, I had to go through all my typescripts and fill in the 'b's' by hand. Stories and articles would only be considered if typed, so I had no choice but to go through with this chore, cursing all the time, the letter 'b' being most appropriate for this purpose: 'Bugger the bloody B!' In all my years of writing, I have never used swear words in print—and now here I am doing just that!

While my typewriter was getting a battering, the suitcase was enjoying a well-earned rest. It was put to use again when I moved to Delhi for three or four years, a period when my creative efforts were at their lowest ebb. As a writer I am greatly influenced by my surroundings and environment, and the Delhi (or rather, New Delhi) of the 1960s failed to get my creative juices flowing.

There was only one thing to do—pack up, and take to the hills.

It was a wise move although not always a restful one. Landlords, leaking roofs, crumbling hillsides, and water shortages all involved moving from one dwelling to another—Maplewood Lodge, Wayside Cottage (on the old Kipling Road), a flat near the Mall, then up to Landour's Prospect Point and down again to Ivy Cottage! The old suitcase was kept fairly busy, now used more as a receptacle for books and papers. The latches had rusted away and I had to use a length of rope to close the suitcase; but it held up wonderfully well, although it was just reinforced hardboard.

For several years it was located under my bed, and whenever I came across some interesting relic, by way of an old magazine or newspaper, I would store it away for reference. My collection included the *Madras Mail Annual* of 1926, an issue of *The Statesman* (1936,

I think) reporting on the horrors of the Quetta earthquake, and a copy of *Life* (1947) carrying a feature on the changes that were taking place in India at the time of Independence. This had a picture of me, looking very angelic, saying my prayers in the school chapel of Bishop Cotton School, Simla, referred to in the article as the 'Eton of the East'. I think I was chosen for the picture partly because I looked angelic and partly because I was one of the handful of English-looking boys left in the school. But there was nothing angelic about me when I was thirteen, just as there is nothing angelic about me now.

Over a period of time the mice had managed to gnaw their way through the fabric of the suitcase and had made a neat little home for themselves among my souvenirs. As they did no great damage, I left them alone; live and let live always having been my motto.

Then last month we had a terrible storm. The window burst open, the glass fell out, the rain came pouring into the room, and by morning the suitcase was half-full of water. The mice had already gone, but everything made of paper had been ruined and had to be thrown away.

The suitcase was put out to dry on the veranda, but it did not look as though it would recover.

'Shall I throw it away?' asked Beena, my granddaughter. 'It's falling to pieces.'

Do you throw away an old friend just because he's a cripple and of no use to anyone any more? For over sixty-four years that cheap hardboard suitcase had been my constant companion, a witness to all my struggles, my successes, my failures, my follies.

'No, we can't throw it away,' I said, 'Put it in the attic, fill it with all those pastries I'm not supposed to eat, and let the mice make merry!'

LIFE IS SWEET, BROTHER

'Tubby' Whitmarsh Knight, who taught us English Literature at B. C. S. in Simla (since 1950), always used to say that a true essayist should be able to write about anything under the sun, ranging from roast pork (Charles Lamb) to an orange (A. A. Milne), to a doorplate (E. V. Lucas), to 'Doing Nothing' (J. B. Priestley). Lamb was, of course, a pure essayist, expressing himself almost entirely in this form. Milne, who wrote humorous essays for *Punch*, was also a successful playwright and children's author, the modest creator of Winnie the Pooh. J. B. Priestley was a very successful novelist, playwright, and broadcaster. Recently I returned to his best-known work, *The Good Companions* (published in 1929 but first discovered by me in the school library in 1949) and found it as delightful as ever, full of good humour and good feeling, qualities that are rare in fiction today.

And what of E. V. Lucas. Forgotten now, but in his time (the early twentieth century) a name to be reckoned with—poet, essayist, anthologist, man of letters! One of my most precious possessions is a little anthology he compiled called *The Open Road*, subtitled 'A Little Book for Wayfarers'. It opens with these lines from *Lavengro*:

'Life is sweet, brother…. There's day and night, brother, both sweet things; sun, moon, and stars, all sweet things; there's likewise a wind on the heath.'

The book is, quite simply, a garland of poetry and prose designed to urge people into the open air, and once there, to make them happy that they came. I have often turned to it when in low spirits or when I am tired or under stress. I never fail to find some verse or prose to cheer me up. There's a delightful little piece on 'The Apple' by a writer called John Burroughs, of whom I know nothing:

'The boy is indeed the true apple-eater, and is not to be questioned how he came by the fruit with which his pockets are filled. It belongs to him, and he may steal it if it cannot be had in any other way. His own juicy flesh craves the juicy flesh of the apple. Sap draws sap. His fruit-eating has little reference to the state of his appetite. Whether he be full of meat or empty of meat he wants the apple just the same. Before meal or after meal it never comes amiss. The farm-boy munches apples all day long.

'The apple is indeed the fruit of youth. As we grow old we crave apples less. It is an ominous sign. When you are ashamed to be seen eating them on the street; when you can carry them in your pocket and your hand not constantly finds its way to them; when your neighbour has apples and you have none, and you make no nocturnal visits to his orchard; when...you can pass a winter's night by the fireside with no thought of the fruit at your elbow, then be assured you are no longer a boy either in heart or in years.'

This little anthology is full of such gems. I wish I could give you my copy, but I know I will never get another; not without a long and patient search.

But while on the subject of apples, here's a little ditty I wrote for Prem's little daughter, Dolly, a long time ago:

> Sweet Dolly, you're the girl for me,
> Kind Dolly, I shall always see
> You climbing in the garden,
> Plucking apples off a tree,
> Sorting out the rosy ones
> And giving them to me!

CHOCOLATES AT MIDNIGHT

One of the great pleasures of life is the afternoon siesta. In Mexico and other Latin American countries it has been perfected to a fine art. In warm countries like ours it is almost a necessity, especially for a farmer toiling in his fields from daybreak to noon. An afternoon nap under a peepul tree or in the shade of a mighty banyan does wonders for body and soul.

I take my siesta on the same bed that I sleep upon at midnight; but if I am travelling I have no difficulty in taking a nap on a plane or in a bus or in a railway waiting room, although I must admit that it's been many years since I travelled by train. Under a tree sounds romantic, but the last time I tried sleeping under a friendly horse chestnut I was woken by chestnuts falling on my head.

Bed is best, especially on a cold winter's day in the hills. And, at night, a hot-water bottle helps.

Given a warm bed, I sleep like a baby. But like a baby I am inclined to wake up at midnight or at one in the morning, feeling rather hungry. And for this purpose I keep a bar of chocolate on my bedside table.

There's nothing like a chunk of chocolate in the middle of the night. It helps me feel that all's right with the world, and I fall asleep again to dream of cricket bats made of chocolate and rainbows made of sugar candy. You must try it sometime, those of you who find difficulty in sleeping.

But a few nights ago I woke up prematurely to hear something nibbling away on my bedside table. *Katr-katr, katr-katr*, came the ominous sound.

I switched on the bedside lamp, and there sat a fat rat, nibbling away at my chocolate!

Now I am generous with most things, and I am happy to share my chocolates with you, gentle reader, but I draw the line at rodents. So I flung a slipper at the rat, who dodged it and took off with some reluctance, and then I had to throw away the remains of the chocolate for fear of catching rat fever or something horrible.

Anyway, the next night I kept a fresh chocolate bar in a drawer of the dressing table, where I felt sure it would be safe. Once again, my dreams were interrupted by the nibble and crunch of small teeth embedding themselves in my chocolate bar. I sprang out of bed, rushed to the dressing table, pulled out the drawer, and out popped Master Rat, the champion chocolate-eater! Away he went, leaving behind only half a bar of chocolate for yours truly.

Apparently he'd found a hole in the back of the drawer, and spurred on by greed, had burrowed his way to the object of his desire.

A trap! A trap was what I needed. So I borrowed my neighbour's rat trap—not the kind that kills, but the kind that imprisons (which may be worse)—and set it up with my favourite chocolate as bait. They say rats prefer cheese, but I wasn't taking any chances.

Anyway, the trap worked, and in the morning I found a disgruntled rat staring at me through the bars of his prison like the Prisoner of Zenda. Picking up the trap, I walked with it for half a mile up the road, and then released Master Rat in the bushes behind a popular bakery. Very irresponsible of me, but I thought the precincts of the bakery would at least keep him occupied.

Three peaceful nights passed. Once again, I enjoyed my midnight chocolate snack. Then—*katr, katr, katr*.... He was back again!

'Once more into the breach, dear friends.' Another trap was borrowed and Master Rat was jailed for a second time. And this time I was taking no chances. I engaged a taxi, drove to the Kempty Waterfall with the rat in its trap. And there flung the protesting rat into the waterfall, much as the villainous Moriarty had flung poor Sherlock Holmes over another waterfall. The last I saw of the rat, he was swimming strongly downstream towards the Yamuna Bridge.

Peace at last. Chocolates forever! Dreams of candyfloss and golden syrups....

And then: *katr, katr, katr*....

I switched on the bedside light.

Two rats were on my desk, having a tug of war with my chocolate bar.

There's only one thing to do.

I'll give up eating chocolates. I'll starve those rats out of existence, even if, in the process, I must suffer from extreme malnutrition.

Later: I have compromised by eating my chocolates in the daytime.

THE GARDEN OF DREAMS

It wasn't so long ago that I found myself in Kathmandu, the colourful capital of Nepal, attending one of those literary festivals that have caught on in countries where books are still written, published, and sometimes read. I had a day or two to myself and I was wandering about in the streets looking for quaint corners—for I am a collector of quaint corners—when I came across a walled enclosure, a long high wall with just an entrance, a heavy door over which was painted the following legend: 'Garden of Dreams'.

Naturally I was curious. If there was a garden, it was behind that wall. And since it had advertised itself, presumably it was open to the public.

On the pavement, not far from the entrance, sat an old woman who was selling trinkets, costume jewellery, and semi-precious stones.

'Mother,' I said, for she seemed older than me, 'What's in that garden of dreams?'

'Flowers,' she said, 'And running water. And dreams.'

Her face was furrowed with the passage of time but

she had a cheerful, winning smile and her forearms were covered with colourful bangles, her fingers with rings of onyx and jade.

'I suppose I can go in,' I said.

'It will open any minute,' she said. 'But first, why don't you buy something? A bracelet for your lady-love?'

'I don't have a lady-love.' But I bought a tiny mirror from her. It was ringed with different coloured stones and crowned with a gaudily painted wooden parrot. As I pocketed my purchase, the door to the garden opened and the old lady said, 'You can go in now and look for your dream.'

There was no one at the door and I couldn't see anyone in the garden, although there were signs of activity at the other end, where a couple of gardeners were pruning a rose bush.

There were roses everywhere—lush golden roses, and pink lollipops, and roses that opened like a woman's labia, and roses that shone in the early morning sun, and some that still held dewdrops between their petals.

I had the garden to myself for almost half an hour and in that time I followed little paths that meandered between beds of crimson poppies, scented petunias of every shade, carpets of multi-coloured phlox, pansies with their funny faces that looked like Oliver Hardy's larkspur, wallflowers, snapdragons....

There was a small waterfall at one end of the garden and it fed a small stream that ran in and out of the spaces between the flower beds. Here and there you could cross the stream by means of small bridges. They gave the garden a distinct Japanese or Oriental look.

I sat down on a bench and tried to take it all in. I am a sensualist by nature, but here there was so much to absorb—colour, fragrance, sunshine, and shade, the flow of water, the pattern of leaves, the twitter of small birds, the passage of a butterfly.... And presently other people were trickling into the garden—some Japanese tourists, laden with cameras; a stout Indian lady in a pink sari, accompanied by a brood of children; a bearded, bespectacled artist with a sketch pad; an English-looking woman lurking beneath a large hat.

The woman in the hat stopped beside me and said, 'Lovely garden, isn't it? So very English....'

'They say the late Rana was inspired by a garden he saw in France,' I commented.

'But French gardens are so formal, aren't they? And this one has something of everything. Even a bit of the willow pattern plate. Was that Chinese or Japanese?'

'Probably a bit of both,' I said. 'Let's just say it's uniquely Nepalese!'

The lady in the hat moved on and the woman in the pink sari plonked herself down on the bench. She was soon joined by two of her noisy children and I made way for them and strolled across to the far end of the garden. Here a fountain was playing and in the pool surrounding it there were several goldfish. Nearby there was a girl on a swing. She could have been sixteen or twenty-six, I couldn't guess her age, she was young and pretty but she was also quite adult in her poise and manner. She made me think of *Alice in Wonderland*. She was dressed all in green, but there was a purple hibiscus in her hair.

'Do you like goldfish?' she asked.

'I do,' I said. 'There is something very restful about them. I can watch them for hours. How they silently glide around in their watery world.'

'And they don't bark,' she said. 'Or make any noise at all.'

I laughed. 'Do you come here often?'

'Quite often,' she said. 'It's your first visit, isn't it?'

'Yes and I'm only here for a day or two. This garden belonged to a princess, I'm told. Does anyone live there now, in the old palace?'

'Sometimes the princess comes. But she's very old now—she doesn't come down from her tower.'

'And you—are you a princess too?'

She laughed and I noticed that her eyes were dark like hazelnuts. There were silver anklets on her feet and a daisy chain around her throat.

'No,' she said, 'I'm just a—' She broke off and looked away and there was a touch of sadness on her face. 'I do all sorts of things,' she said, sounding quite cheerful again. 'Have you seen the birds?'

'You mean the sparrows?'

'No, the aviary. There are lots of small birds. Come, I'll show you.'

She jumped off the swing and beckoned and I found myself by her side, holding her hand.

Had she taken my hand or had I taken hers? I wasn't sure. It was just something that had happened.

The touch of her hand sent a strange thrill through my entire person. It wasn't like any hand that I'd ever held. It was a young hand, the palms soft and the fingers strong; but it was also the hand of her ancestors and I felt that it had stories to tell. It was also taking something out of me. I felt younger, even reckless. I clung to her hand as though I was clinging to life itself; I did not want to let go.

A variety of small, colourful birds flitted about the spacious aviary, some on swings, some on the branches of a small blossoming plum tree. Plum blossoms were flung far and wide. There was a great amount of birdsong, if you could call it that. Really just twittering and chirping, like a bunch of cocktail party humans having a gossip session. A pair of lovebirds appeared to be enamoured of each other; they kept kissing each other with their tiny beaks.

'See, they are making love!' exclaimed my companion, her hand pressing into mine. Her hazel eyes were excited. I was tempted to kiss her but at that moment the large hatted lady loomed over us and we became self-conscious.

'Sexy little creatures, aren't they?' she said. 'Just like a couple of teenagers.'

She was obviously referring to the lovebirds, for I was no teenager; but my companion led me away, still holding me by the hand.

She took me into a shady arbour, and we sat there for

some time, and she told me her name, Kiran, and that she lived close by and came to the garden almost every day. I did not ask her too many questions. Conscious that I was much older than her and that she knew nothing about me, I did not want to frighten her off with too much familiarity. A gazelle will come to you if you are very still but if you move towards it, the beautiful creature will dart away. And this was a gazelle I was talking to.

She asked me questions and I told her about myself, that I worked for an Indian publishing firm and that I was in Kathmandu for a few days—with just a day or two to go.

'Will you come again tomorrow?' she asked.

'If you like,' I said, 'And then perhaps you can show me the marketplace. It's close by, isn't it?'

'Yes, quite close. But I like it here in the garden.' She had released my hand and I felt that something was going from me. And then the lady in the pink sari barged in with her kids, and the spell was broken.

She walked with me as far as the garden door. I looked back at the tall, old building behind the garden.

'Do you live there?' I asked.

She nodded, smiling wistfully.

'It looks very old,' I said. 'So you really are a princess?'

She laughed and her dark eyes lit up in the sunshine. 'I am anything I want to be.'

'Till tomorrow, then,' I said.

'Till tomorrow....'

And so we parted. Out on the street I bought another trinket, and the old lady noticed that I looked happy and she gave me a toothless grin and asked, 'Did you find your dream?'

'Better than a dream,' I said and made my way back to the hotel where I had a meeting with local publishers.

∽

I forget how I spent the rest of that day. I kept thinking about the girl in the garden. We had struck up a good rapport and I wanted to see her again and take our friendship forward.

So next morning, after breakfast, I sallied forth to the garden of dreams.

She wasn't there.

I walked around the garden several times. I hung about near the pool and the aviary and sat on a bench for at least an hour. Visitors came and went. Tourists from China and Japan; talking, admiring. Loud-voiced Americans. Some quiet, reserved Africans. A writer from India came up to me and thrust a folder into my hands. 'For you to publish,' he said. 'It will sell in millions!' He must have followed me into the garden. I promised to read his masterpiece.

Then I paced about, studying rose bushes, herbaceous borders, lovebirds. No one came.

It was getting on to noon when I gave up and left the garden.

No, I did not buy any trinkets.

The old woman looked up at me and said, 'No good dream today?'

I shook my head and said, 'Yesterday I met a girl in the garden. She said her name was Kiran. She was to meet me again today. She was a princess, I think. Do you know her?'

The old woman shook her head. 'There is no princess living here. Kiran? I do not know the name. Perhaps she could not come today. Why not try tomorrow?'

'But I must leave tomorrow.'

'It is sad, then. She means much to you, this girl?'

'I think so.'

She nodded wisely. 'Many hearts have been broken in the garden of dreams.' And she said no more.

∽

I wandered the streets of Kathmandu. I wasn't looking for anyone. I just couldn't stand being alone in my hotel room or in the company of writers and publishers.

Towards evening I passed the garden of dreams. The door was shut, the walls were too high to see anything. I supposed she did not want to see me again. That overture of friendship, the pressure of her hand, the tenderness in her eyes, her every gesture had spoken of liking, if not of love. Perhaps it meant nothing after all. Just a way of passing the time.... And here I was, a middle-aged moron, fretting like an adolescent who had just fallen in love!

My plane was to leave at noon.

There was time for one last visit to the garden, albeit a hurried one.

It was far too early. The street was deserted. The garden door was locked from within. The old lady with her wares was yet to arrive. The sun was only just coming up.

Further along the street, where the garden enclosure ended, someone was sweeping the pavement using a long-handled broom. Fallen leaves and plastic waste were being swept into an imposing heap—all so symbolic of the new century.

I approached the early morning sweeper. Perhaps he could help me.

It wasn't a 'he'. The person, dressed in a uniform of sorts, turned to me when I spoke and I was shocked into silence; for it was none other than Kiran.

She was as surprised as I was. She dropped the broom. A look of panic crossed her face and then vanished just as quickly.

'You are here—so early—it does not open till ten.'

'I came to see you, not the garden,' I said. 'And you promised to meet me yesterday.'

'I could not come. I was sent into town on some work. My father works for the old king's family. But as you can see, I am not a princess. That was just a game.' She gave me an enigmatic smile.

'So let the game continue,' I said and held out my hand.

She took it, held it for a moment, then let it fall. 'You are a good person,' she said simply.

'And you are a princess,' I said, 'and I want to see you again. But my plane leaves shortly. If I come again in a few months' time, will you be here?'

'In the garden or outside?' Her good humour was returning.

'Near the aviary. Where the lovebirds sing.'

'They don't sing,' she said, laughing. 'They kiss each other all the time.'

Well, I didn't kiss her, although I longed to do so. The street was filling up, people were staring at us. There were no cell phones then, but I gave her my home address and asked her to write to me. Then I rushed back to the hotel, collected my bag, sent for a taxi, and headed for the airport.

Soon the garden and Kiran were just a dream.

∽

But it was a dream that wouldn't go away.

The monsoon rains came and went and an autumn breeze swept across the hills and knocked over the windows of my hilltop home. There was no word from Kiran. Perhaps she did not write letters. Perhaps she did not write at all!

On my desk was the little mirror I'd bought from the old lady outside the garden. It sparkled in the morning sun; it glowed at the time of sunset. A little bird—just a sparrow—flew in at the open window, examined the wooden parrot, pecked at the mirror, and flew away. Sometimes I thought I saw someone in the mirror—just a figure, a slight figure in green, but she was always walking away. Mirrors can play tricks.

And this planet, this earth and its hidden fires, can be cruel.

An earthquake struck the Himaal.

It ran through the heart of Nepal, razing towns, villages, palatial buildings, and humble dwellings. Thousands perished. Thousands lost their homes, their living, their loved ones. These sudden horrific natural calamities almost always strike the poorest, most vulnerable countries—Haiti, Mozambique, small island nations, landlocked mountain lands, Nepal....

As the news came through on my television, I feared the worst. Would Kiran have survived? And what of other friends and associates? I phoned them, made enquires, but news trickled through very slowly. People were too busy salvaging what was left of their homes. And many slept in the open as aftershocks ran through the country, bringing down structures already weakened by the earth's convulsions.

And then there was a period of quiet as things began to settle. Normalcy could not return, but the resilient people of this small nation went about rebuilding their homes and shattered lives.

There was no news of Kiran or the garden or the old lady on the street. They were not people who normally made the news. I would have to visit Kathmandu again, to see if the garden and its occupants were still there.

But before I could do that I had a visitor.

The steps to my room are steep and uneven and I was struggling up them after a visit to the bazaar when I noticed someone sitting on the top step, a backpack by her side.

It was Kiran. She looked tired and weak, but more beautiful than ever.

'I've come to see you,' she said.

'For a long, long time, I hope.' And I took her by the hand and led her into my home, my garden of books.

And that was how Kiran came into my life.

If you meet her, she will tell you about the garden of dreams (it's still there) and the old lady on the street (she's still there) and the lovebirds and the goldfish and the little stream. And perhaps she will take you there some day; for she is a girl who can make dreams come true.

CROSSING THE ROAD

Samuel was a snail of some individuality. Some considered him to be the bad snail in the family, but that was because he did not listen to his elders and liked to do things in his own way, trying out new plants or venturing into forbidden places. Birds and butterflies recognized no man-made borders, so why should snails? They'd been around longer than humans and were likely to be around even longer.

Not that Samuel had any global ambitions. It was just that the cabbage patch in which he and his fellow snails had been living did not appeal to him any more. He was heartily sick of cabbage leaves. And just across a busy road—his international boundary—was a field full of delicious looking lettuce. And any snail would prefer lettuce to cabbage.

The trouble was, it was a very busy road, linking one city to another, and on it flowed a constant stream of cars, trucks, motorcycles, bicycles, vans, even the occasional steamroller. Samuel did not like the idea of being crushed under a steamroller. There were better ways of exiting planet Earth—being swallowed by a large stork, for instance.

And then, of course, snails can't run. With the help of a little of their own juices, they glide slowly and leisurely over grass and weed and pebbles, in search of a juicy leaf or the company of a fellow snail. They were not made to run. They are not predators like the larger carnivores. Nor do they prey on each other like humans. They are all for minding their own business. And now here was Samuel, making it his business to invade that lettuce patch on the other side of the road.

Well, nothing ventured, nothing gained. And ignoring the warnings of friends and familiars, Samuel set out to cross that life-threatening road. He could, of course, have waited until it was dark, but the road would have been no safer then. A constant stream of container trucks came thundering down the highway all through the night.

Tentacles waving, he began his stately crawl across the road.

Almost immediately he was nearly run over by a boy on a bicycle. Instinctively, Samuel withdrew into his little shell. Not that it would have made any difference. It might have protected him from a small bird, but not from a cycle tyre.

Samuel looked up and down the road. It was a single width road, and vehicles could approach from either direction. It appeared to be clear at the moment.

Samuel advanced, covering a distance of some twelve inches in sixty seconds flat.

Then—*woosh*—a car sped by, its tyres missing Samuel by inches. He was almost blown away by a cloud of dust and exhaust fumes.

And then came another car. Samuel cringed. And survived. And wondered if he should turn around and go back the way he came. But snails aren't great thinkers. The lettuce patch was all that mattered.

Samuel had advanced by two or three feet when there came a deep rumbling sound and he felt the ground quiver beneath him. A huge truck was bearing down on him!

Sometimes it is an advantage to be small. Samuel was somewhere in the middle of the road, and nowhere near the wheels when the truck thundered over him. All the same he was dazed and shaken, unable to move any further. Soon another truck would be coming along. Or was it a tractor that was chugging along towards him?

Just then there was a squeal of brakes, a blare of horns, and a tremendous crash. The truck had hit an oncoming car and both had veered off the road and were lying in a ditch. For a time all traffic ceased. Samuel emitted a slimy jet and began to crawl again. Then there was a burst of activity.

A motorcycle came tearing down the road, whizzing past a bewildered Samuel, and then stopping at the accident site. A policeman dismounted. In the distance a siren wailed. An ambulance was on its way.

And then it began to rain, a gentle patter on the tarmac. Refreshed, Samuel slid forward. The rain came down harder, and a fallen peepul leaf came sailing towards Samuel. It stopped beside him and Samuel crawled to the leaf. A spurt of rainwater picked up the leaf and sent it sailing across the remainder of the road and onto the grass verge.

Excelsior!

Samuel was home if not dry.

The lettuce field stretched before him. Motor horns and ambulance sirens melted into the distance. Humans could take care of themselves. So could snails! It would take him weeks to munch his way through a small corner of that lettuce patch, but he was going to try. To the winner the spoils!

The rain stopped and he began his feast.

The lettuce was all right, but it wasn't much better than the cabbage field he had left a little over an hour ago. Had the journey been worthwhile? Could he cross that road again? The odds were against survival.

He'd just have to settle down in this new and unfamiliar world. The grass is always greener on the other side—until you get there!

THE DOPPELGÄNGER

It was in 1960, or thereabouts, that I first met a doppelgänger.

There, I have at least spelt it right. It's a German word but you can find it in the *Oxford Dictionary of English*, where so many exotic words turn up.

I was twenty-six at the time. I'd had a novel published in London, but very few people bought it, and my freelancing efforts in New Delhi were appreciated but seldom rewarded. I had taken a job with CARE, an American relief agency, and they sent me to Darjeeling (among other places) to see what help could be given to the Tibetan refugees who had arrived there.

So I was a nobody, trying to be a somebody.

When I entered the portals of the old Everest Hotel, I found it full of somebodys. There was Shammi Kapoor and his Bollywood crew, engaged in making a romantic film called *Professor*. And there was Satyajit Ray and his crew from Kolkata, engaged in making an artistic film called *Kanchenjunga*.

Kanchenjunga was the name of the majestic peak

visible from Darjeeling, and while I was there I had a glimpse of it as well as a few glimpses of the shooting of these two contrasting films. But this is not the story of those films, or of my work with the Tibetans, but of an encounter that took place because of them.

Free one afternoon, I was strolling along the Darjeeling Mall when I heard a stentorious voice call out, 'Mr Bond! Have you got my Henry Green?'

It was Marie Seton.

I had met Marie Seton a few times in New Delhi, having been introduced to her by the chief of CARE, who had written a book about Laos. Marie was much older than me, but she was good company, and we would often meet at the India Coffee House and have long, gossipy chats over a pot of strong coffee. She was a film enthusiast, had edited Eisenstein's unfinished *Que Viva Mexico*, which I had seen in London, and was now engaged in writing the filmography of Satyajit Ray's films. That accounted for her presence in Darjeeling.

'Your Henry Green?' I countered, as we came face to face, 'I have never read Henry Green.' He was an author who was currently in fashion, but I had yet to meet someone who had read his works.

'I am sure I lent it to you,' she said vaguely. 'Or maybe it was to Khushwant. Anyway, what are you doing up here? You're not with that lot from Bombay, are you—singing and dancing on the railway tracks?'

'No, of course not.' But I felt a little guilty, because only that morning I had exchanged a few words with the charming Geeta Bali, Mr Kapoor's wife. She was not in the film—had retired from filming because of poor health—but was still very attractive in her own unique way.

'I can't sing and I can't dance,' I said. 'But come and have a coffee, and I'll tell you why I am here.'

So we sat at the wayside café and chatted about books and films and the British royal family (she was an expert on the royal family and knew all of them, apparently), and even promised to introduce me to the great Satyajit Ray later that evening.

And so we parted, and I went about my work, returning to the hotel at about six in the evening. The lobby was full of all the film people, but there was no sign of Marie Seton, and when I enquired at the reception I was told that no one by that name was staying there.

Never mind. She must've been staying somewhere else, in a more modest hotel, and presumably at her own expense. I went for a long walk in Darjeeling's December mist, and forgot all about our encounter.

A few weeks later I was back in New Delhi, strolling around Connaught Place in search of a bookshop, when I heard that familiar voice. 'What have you done with my Henry Green?'

It was Marie Seton again.

'You know I don't have it,' I protested. 'I haven't read Henry Green and have no desire to read his damn book. So come and have a coffee and bring me up to date on all the royal gossip.'

We went into Nirula's and caught up with each other's news.

'So tell me,' I asked, 'how did the shooting go in Darjeeling? We were supposed to meet, but I couldn't find you at the hotel—'

'What hotel? What are you talking about?'

'Last month in Darjeeling. Don't you remember? We met on the Mall, while Ray was filming *Kanchenjunga*.'

'My dear boy, I've never been to Darjeeling. You've been imagining things—reading too much Anaïs Nin! I wish I'd been there, though. Watching Ray at work—just what I need for my book. But it was not to be. I was down with flu at the time.'

'But you were there—we met on the Mall—you asked me for your wretched Henry Green!'

'Nonsense! I couldn't have been in two places at once.'

And then it occurred to me—perhaps she was a doppelgänger, capable of being in two places at once! I gave a little shudder. Somehow a doppelgänger was scarier than a ghost; a living person with supernatural qualities. Was she, even now, real? Or was she just an apparition sipping coffee with me? Of course she had been in Darjeeling that day. And perhaps she was somewhere else, even now. She could be having tea at Buckingham Palace! No wonder she was so well-informed on royalty....

I got up to leave; made some lame excuse about a prior appointment; promised to meet her again.

'Farewell, dear boy,' she said with a sinister smile. 'And don't forget my Henry Green.'

ᔆ

Well, I had yet to come across a copy of a Henry Green novel, although I know that such a writer did exist; forgotten, if he was ever remembered. And I did not see Marie Seton again for a couple of years, although I felt sure she was doppelgänging all over the place.

And then one day I was at the New Delhi railway station, accompanied by a young writer called Sasthi Brata, who was to make a name for himself with a confessional novel called *My God Died Young*. We were seeing off Professor P. Lal, an academic whose Writer's Workshop in Kolkata was the last resort for many an aspiring writer.

We had paid our respects to the great man, and the train was beginning to move, when I caught sight of Marie Seton in the next compartment. She was reading a book. I called out to her, and she looked up, but I don't think she saw me, as just then the train picked up speed, and her compartment swept past me.

'Who did you call out to?' asked my companion.

'Marie Seton,' I said. 'She's always turning up in unexpected places.'

'It couldn't have been her,' said Sasthi B. 'She died on a film set in Bhutan about two months ago.'

'It was Marie Seton in that carriage,' I insisted.

'Then you saw her ghost,' he said. 'Or someone who looked just like her.'

So now even her ghost was a doppelgänger!

I gave up. And when I got home to my room in East Patel Nagar I wasn't a bit surprised to find a Henry Green novel on my desk.

While rounding of this little tale it has occurred to me that everyone mentioned in it—writers, actors, directors, singers, academics—have all made their exits from life on this particular planet and have, hopefully, moved on to a better place—or to complete nothingness—leaving behind some memorials to their artistry: books, films, songs, poems, creative contributions big or small to the passing show.

There is a Latin proverb—

Ars longa, vita brevis....

Art is long, life is short.

Or, to turn it around: life is short, but art is long.

HAUNTED PLACES

THE ROCKING CHAIR

Yes, sometimes old houses do give you a feeling of still being occupied by the ghosts or spirits of long-dead occupants—people who once lived and loved beneath that weathered roof and between those listening walls.

The walls listen to us by day; and when, late at night, the residents are asleep, they and the rest of the house come to life, gossip among themselves, and discuss the strengths and weaknesses of the human guests. Those walls, those pictures, those old tables and armchairs have seen triumph and tragedy, and sometimes they resonate with these things and release some of what they have absorbed.

Like that old rocking chair I picked up in the antique shop near Landour's clock tower. I had no desire to purchase or own a rocking chair, but when I spotted it in a corner of the shop I couldn't resist sitting down in it; and finding that it suited my ample proportions I remained seated for some time, becoming increasingly aware that I belonged to it in some way and that I ought to possess it.

We haggled over the price, and I ended up paying more than it seemed to be worth, although the shop owner maintained that it had once belonged to a royal family. A Nepali labourer carried it on his back and delivered it to my rooms higher up the hillside, and I found a place for it in a corner of my sunny bedroom.

Every afternoon I would settle into that rocking chair, read a little, and then rock myself to sleep until Beena woke me up with a cup of tea. I had the rocking chair all to myself—by day, that is....

It was only at night, late at night, that someone else seemed to occupy it.

The chair had been in my room for a few days, getting used to its new surroundings I suppose. Then, one night, I was woken by a rhythmical creaking sound, and switching on the bed light I saw that the rocking chair was in motion, oscillating back and forth as though it had an occupant.

Well, there was no one in it, and I came to the conclusion that it had been set in motion by the light breeze from my open window, kept open on summer nights.

This happened on several occasions and I was getting quite used to it when, late one night, the rocking was more rapid and vigorous than usual, and I turned on the light to see a tiny old woman sitting in the chair, rocking to and fro, and grinning at me in a rather childish manner. There were rings on her fingers and she appeared to be dressed in an expensive gown. But she had no teeth, and this gave a sort of malevolent leer to her grin.

I shot out of bed, and as I did so the figure of the old woman vanished. The empty chair kept rocking.

Next day, I removed it to the attic. If the ghost of old ladies wanted to use it, they were welcome to do so, but not in my bedroom. And when I spoke to the antique shop owner about this vision of mine, he confessed that the rocking chair had once belonged to the Rani of —, and that she had died in it, at an advanced age.

The rocking chair is still in my attic. I don't go up there at night. But the other day, while reading in my little sunroom, I heard the creaking of the chair and felt bold enough to climb the stairs to see if it had a visitor.

It was only the neighbourhood cat, a large tabby, curled up in the middle of the chair, enjoying its motion.

Perhaps the old rani likes having a little company, because the cat is there quite often, purring contentedly, while an unseen hand strokes it behind the ears. I don't disturb them. Cats see more than we do. And if the rocking chair can give pleasure to the ghost of an old rani, she's more than welcome to it.

But I don't go up to the attic at night. I might just see her again.

∽

A HAUNTED HOUSE

Back in the 1950s, when I was still in my teens, I would often wander up the Rajpur Road, a quiet tree-lined highway with a few old bungalows scattered here and there. One of them, a two-storeyed building, had lain empty and abandoned for several years. It was reputed to be haunted, and no one was interested in buying or renting it. Even passers-by gave it a wide berth.

I had seen the house from outside, but I had never ventured into its grounds. The story of the haunting, if indeed it was a haunting, went like this: an elderly English couple, childless, had owned the house and lived in it for many years. But when they grew old their income from investments dwindled, and at the time of Independence they were really hard up. Being old and reclusive, they had been forgotten by the rest of the community, most of whom were busy making arrangements to leave the country. By the end of 1948 most of the Anglo-Indians and Europeans in Dehra had left for 'home' (the U. K.) but the old couple had stayed on, more from compulsion than desire. They had, indeed, been quite forgotten—until, one day, a bill collector (for light or water or some unpaid services) entered the house and found the old couple dead in their large four-poster bed. They had died of starvation, probably within a few hours of each other. The post-mortem revealed that their stomachs were empty.

It was a sad story and a depressing one, and people

did not want to talk about it. It was nobody's fault, but we all feel a little guilty when a fellow human dies of neglect.

I was curious about the deserted house but I was afraid to enter it on my own. Instead I wandered about the grounds, a wilderness of overgrown shrubs and dying rose bushes. Here and there a flowering plant had struggled to survive but tall grasses and weeds were taking over.

As I was about to leave from the broken gate, I was hailed by my cousin Ronald, who was passing by on his bicycle.

'Hey, Ruskin, what are you doing there? Have you become a ghost-hunter now?'

'Just looking around,' I said, feeling a bit foolish. Did I really expect to see a couple of ghosts?

'I'll come and join you,' said Ronald. 'But first let me fetch some grub. You can't look for ghosts on an empty stomach.' And off he rode, in the direction of the Ellora Bakery.

He was an impulsive fellow, and I wasn't sure if he'd come back; but twenty minutes later he came cycling through the open gate, his shopping basket topped up with pastries, buns, cheese rolls, chicken patties, sandwiches.... Ronald's pocket money far exceeded mine. His father owned a cinema; my stepfather owed money all over the town.

'Let's go inside,' said Ronald. 'It's hot out here. And ghosts don't sunbathe.'

So far I'd remained in the garden, reluctant to venture into the house on my own. But Ronald showed no compunction about going in; I simply followed.

Most of the furniture had gone from the rooms. In the hall was a sofa with the stuffing exposed; in the dining room a table and a couple of broken chairs; in the bedroom a large double-bed without any mattress or coverings. Anything that could be sold had been taken away, probably by vandals.

We weren't vandals, but we were a couple of ghouls, picnicking in the ruined home of people who had died in tragic circumstances. But Ronald was very blasé about the whole thing. For him it was enormous fun.

'Tuck in, Ruskin,' he said, spreading out all the delicacies on a dressing table, its mirror broken. 'They must have looked in it every day, except towards the end.'

I was beginning to lose my appetite. Those old people had starved to death, and here we were, glutting ourselves on cakes and savouries. When I commented on this fact, Ronald said, 'Pooh! It wasn't our fault, what happened. They're welcome to join us, if they are still around.'

But no one was around. A haunted house? The rooms were entirely without any atmosphere. Just dust everywhere, and cobwebs.

A large spider ran across the bed.

'We'll leave a pastry for the spider,' said Ronald. And since you're not eating anything, we'll leave the rest for the old folk.'

'Don't leave any food here,' I said. 'It seems rather—'

'What?'

'Well, disrespectful.'

'You are an old-fashioned fellow, Ruskin. Come on, let's go. I want to catch the matinee at three. They're showing *Ben-Hur* at the Odeon.'

I walked with him to the gate. No, I had no premonition of disaster, but I declined his invitation to take a ride on his pillion, and as for *Ben-Hur*, those quasi-Biblical spectacles, with their 'casts of millions', failed to excite me.

Ronald hopped on to his bicycle and, as was his habit, rode off at speed as though he were in a cycle race. Always up to new tricks, he grabbed the fender of a small truck and allowed it to carry him some distance. As it picked up speed, he let go and swerved into the centre of the road. At the same time an army truck, coming from the opposite direction, slammed straight into the cyclist, sending him sprawling and then running over the helpless boy.

It all happened very suddenly. I stood there, petrified. People ran to Ronald's aid, and within minutes the truck driver and his mates had taken the badly injured boy to the army hospital in the nearby cantonment. But Ronald did not survive the impact of the collision. It was no one's fault, just the logical outcome of his reckless nature.

And we hadn't seen any ghosts. But had they seen us? Do we see the stars at noon? They are there all the same, looking down at us, and it is we who cannot see them.

Ronald's parents were devastated by the tragedy, for

he had been their only son. I had never been very close to him, but I had seen the accident and it scarred my memories for many years. It helped to convince me that life is not about rewards and punishments, but about consequences.

ဢ

A HAUNTED PLANET

There is no ghost more dangerous or intractable than the Covid virus that has infiltrated the human race in the course of the last two years. Invisible! Unstoppable! Everywhere at once. Baffling and teasing scientists, rendering the gurus and godmen bereft of platitudes, bringing out the best in some of us, the worst in others.

A true ghost, travelling the globe without passport, without hindrance. Happiest in a crowd, moving unseen amongst the revellers or protestors or worshippers, regardless of what brings people together. A lover of crowds, this ghost, but it will follow you to a distant village or lonely hilltop if it so wishes.

Is it nature in revolt, now telling us that we are not the masters after all, and that there is a limit to how much we can destroy and poison and desiccate this unique planet...who knows?

Perhaps the haunting will subside and we will know then. Or is it too late to learn from our follies?

ဢ

2 A.M.

Two o'clock in the morning—the darkest hour, when our energy, mental and physical, is at its lowest. For those who are critically ill, the tide is running out. For those who cannot sleep it is a dead, depressing hour.

Because of a prostate problem I have to get up at least three times in the night to ease the pressure on my bladder. Twelve o'clock or thereabouts; at about 2 a.m.; and then at about four in the morning. At twelve o'clock there are some who are still awake. At four in the morning there are some who are getting up because they have a busy day ahead—a plane to catch or a long road journey. But at two or three in the morning nobody's about. The silence is deafening. Even the dogs have stopped barking; the neighbourhood dogs who bark simply because other dogs are barking.

And then, the other night, something unusual happened. I had just returned from the bathroom and was about to hop into bed when I heard a loud knocking on the front door.

A visitor at 2 a.m.? I couldn't think of anyone who would want to drop in for a chat in the dead of night. It had to be an emergency. I put on my dressing gown, went to the front door and opened it without hesitation.

Standing there, about nine or ten feet tall, was a woman in black, towering over me. It could have been a man, but I had the impression it was a woman, possibly a nun, because she was dressed in black from head to foot. I couldn't see her face, but I saw her hands—large hands with long scabrous fingers.

I had the fright of my life. This was Death's Dark Angel, if ever there was one. I tried to close the door, but she had slipped that questing hand between the doors and was pushing against them. In desperation I caught one of her fingers and bent it backwards, and finally she drew her hand away and I was able to shut and bolt the door.

I returned to my bedroom, unsure if I was enacting a dream or experiencing something very tangible and real. I sat on the edge of my bed, knowing I wouldn't be able to sleep. I turned off the light. And then, just as I did so, the knocking started again. But this time it was at the window. Someone was standing on the window ledge, two storeys above the road, tapping on the windowpanes.

The curtains were drawn. I made a dash for them, pulled them aside, and opened the window. Opened it wide. This was an impulsive act, not a brave one. But I felt I had to confront this awful visitor.

There was no one there. She had made her presence felt, and then she had gone.

2 a.m.

The dead of night. When the dead still roam.

TALES OF FOSTERGANJ

FOSTER OF FOSTERGANJ

Straddling a spur of the Mussoorie range, as it dips into the Doon valley, Fosterganj came into existence some two hundred years ago and was almost immediately forgotten. And today it is not very different from what it was in 1961, when I lived there briefly.

A quiet corner, where I could live like a recluse and write my stories—that was what I was looking for. And in Fosterganj I thought I'd found my retreat: a cluster of modest cottages, a straggling little bazaar, a post office, a crumbling castle (supposedly haunted), a mountain stream at the bottom of the hill, a winding footpath that took you either uphill or down. What more could one ask for? It reminded me a little of an English village, and indeed that was what it had once been; a tiny settlement on the outskirts of the larger hill station. But the British had long since gone, and the residents were now a fairly mixed lot, as we shall see.

I forget what took me to Fosterganj in the first place. Destiny, perhaps; although I'm not sure why destiny would have bothered to guide an itinerant writer to an obscure hamlet in the hills. Chance would be a better word. For chance plays a great part in all our lives. And it was just by chance that I found myself in the Fosterganj bazaar one fine morning early in May. The oaks and maples were in new leaf; geraniums flourished on sunny balconies; a boy delivering milk whistled a catchy Dev Anand song; a mule train clattered down the street. The chill of winter had gone and there was warmth in the sunshine that played upon old walls.

I sat in a tea shop, tested my teeth on an old bun, and washed it down with milky tea. The bun had been around for some time, but so had I, so we were quits. At the age of forty I could digest almost anything.

The tea shop owner, Melaram, was a friendly sort, as are most tea shop owners. He told me that not many tourists made their way down to Fosterganj. The only attraction was the waterfall, and you had to be fairly fit in order to scramble down the steep and narrow path that led to the ravine where a little stream came tumbling over the rocks. I would visit it one day, I told him.

'Then you should stay here a day or two,' said Melaram. 'Explore the stream. Walk down to Rajpur. You'll need a good walking stick. Look, I have several in my shop. Cherry wood, walnut wood, oak.' He saw me wavering. 'You'll also need one to climb the next hill—it's called Pari Tibba.' I was charmed by the name—Fairy Hill.

I hadn't planned on doing much walking that day—the walk down to Fosterganj from Mussoorie had already taken almost an hour—but I liked the look of a sturdy cherry-wood walking stick, and I bought one for two rupees. Those were the days of simple living. You don't see two-rupee notes any more. You don't see walking sticks either. Hardly anyone walks.

I strolled down the small bazaar, without having to worry about passing cars and lorries or a crush of people. Two or three schoolchildren were sauntering home, burdened by their school bags bursting with homework. A cow and a couple of stray dogs examined the contents of an overflowing dustbin. A policeman sitting on a stool outside a tiny police outpost yawned, stretched, stood up, looked up and down the street in anticipation of crimes to come, scratched himself in the anal region, and sank back upon his stool.

A man in a crumpled shirt and threadbare trousers came up to me, looked me over with his watery grey eyes, and said, 'Sir, would you like to buy some gladioli bulbs?' He held up a basket full of bulbs which might have been onions. His chin was covered with a grey stubble, some of his teeth were missing, the remaining ones yellow with neglect.

'No, thanks,' I said. 'I live in a tiny flat in Delhi. No room for flowers.'

'A world without flowers,' he shook his head. 'That's what it's coming to.'

'And where do you plant your bulbs?'

'I grow gladioli, sir, and sell the bulbs to good people like you. My name's Foster. I own the lands all the way down to the waterfall.'

For a landowner he did not look very prosperous. But his name intrigued me. 'Isn't this area called Fosterganj?' I asked.

'That's right. My grandfather was the first to settle here. He was a grandson of Bonnie Prince Charlie who fought the British at Bannockburn. I'm the last Foster of Fosterganj. Are you sure you won't buy my daffodil bulbs?'

'I thought you said they were gladioli.'

'Some gladioli, some daffodils.'

They looked like onions to me, but to make him happy I parted with two rupees (which seemed the going rate in Fosterganj) and relieved him of his basket of bulbs. Foster shuffled off, looking a bit like Chaplin's tramp but not half as dapper. He clearly needed the two rupees. Which made me feel less foolish about spending money that I should have held on to. Writers were poor in those days. Though I didn't feel poor.

Back at the tea shop I asked Melaram if Foster really owned a lot of land.

'He has a broken-down cottage and the right-of-way. He charges people who pass through his property. Spends all the money on booze. No one owns the hillside, it's government land. Reserved forest. But everyone builds on it.'

Just as well, I thought, as I returned to town with

my basket of onions. Who wanted another noisy hill station? One Mall Road was more than enough. Back in my hotel room, I was about to throw the bulbs away, but on second thoughts decided to keep them. After all, even an onion makes a handsome plant.

BATHROOM WITH A VIEW

Next morning I found myself trudging down from Mussoorie to Fosterganj again. I didn't quite know why I was attracted to the place—but it was quaint, isolated, a forgotten corner of an otherwise changing hill town; and I had always been attracted to forgotten corners.

There was no hotel or guest house in the area, which in itself was a blessing; but I needed somewhere to stay, if I was going to spend some time there.

Melaram directed me to the local bakery. Hassan, the baker, had a room above his shop that had lain vacant since he built it a few years ago. An affable man, Hassan was the proud father of a dozen children; I say dozen at random, because I never did get to ascertain the exact number as they were never in one place at the same time. They did not live in the room above the bakery, which was much too small, but in a rambling old building below the bazaar, which housed a number of large families—the baker's, the tailor's, the postman's, among others.

I was shown the room. It was scantily furnished, the bed taking up almost half the space. A small table and chair stood near the window. Windows are important. I find it impossible to live in a room without a window. This one provided a view of the street and the buildings on the other side. Nothing very inspiring, but at least it wouldn't be dull.

A narrow bathroom was attached to the room. Hassan was very proud of it, because he had recently installed a flush tank and western-style potty. I complimented him on the potty and said it looked very comfortable. But what really took my fancy was the bathroom window. It hadn't been opened for some time, and the glass panes were caked with dirt. But when finally we got it open, the view was remarkable. Below the window was a sheer drop of two or three hundred feet. Ahead, an open vista, a wide valley, and then the mountains striding away towards the horizon. I don't think any hotel in town had such a splendid view. I could see myself sitting for hours on that potty, enraptured, enchanted, having the valley and the mountains all to myself. Almost certain constipation of course, but I would take that risk.

'Forty rupees a month,' said Hassan, and I gave him two months' rent on the spot.

'I'll move in next week,' I said. 'First I have to bring my books from Delhi.'

On my way back to the town I took a shortcut through the forest. A swarm of yellow butterflies drifted across the path. A woodpecker pecked industriously on the bark of a tree, searching for young cicadas. Overhead, wild duck flew north, on their way across Central Asia, all travelling without passports. Birds and butterflies recognize no borders.

I hadn't been this way before, and I was soon lost. Two village boys returning from town with their milk cans gave me the wrong directions. I was put on the right path by a girl who was guiding a cow home. There was something about her fresh face and bright smile that I found tremendously appealing. She was less than beautiful but more than pretty, if you know what I mean. A face to remember.

A little later I found myself in an open clearing, with a large pool in the middle. Its still waters looked very deep. At one end there were steps, apparently for bathers. But the water did not look very inviting. It was a sunless place, several old oaks shutting out the light. Fallen off leaves floated on the surface. No birds sang. It was a strange, haunted sort of place. I hurried on.

LATE FOR A FUNERAL

When I said that Fosterganj appeared to be the sort of sleepy hollow where nothing ever happened, it only served to show that appearances can be deceptive. When I returned that summer, carrying books and writing materials, I found the little hamlet in a state of turmoil.

There was a rabies scare.

On my earlier visit I had noticed the presence of a number of stray dogs. The jackal population must have been fairly large too. And jackals are carriers of the rabies virus.

I had barely alighted from the town's only Ambassador taxi when I had to jump in again. Down the road came some ten to fifteen dogs, of no particular breed but running with the urgency of greyhounds, ears flattened, tails between their legs, teeth bared in terror, for close behind them came the dog-catchers, three or four men carrying staves and what appeared to be huge butterfly nets. Even as I gaped in astonishment one of the dogs took a tumble and, howling with fright, was scooped up and dumped in a metal cage on wheels which stood at the side of the road.

The dog chase swept past me, one young man staying behind to secure the trapped canine. Some people have faces that bear an uncanny resemblance to the features of different animals. This particular youth had something of the wolf in his countenance. The dog obviously thought so too, for it whimpered and cowered in a corner of its rusty cage. I am not a great dog lover but I felt sorry for this frightened creature and put my hand through the bars to try and pat it. Immediately it bared its teeth and lunged at my hand. I withdrew it in a hurry.

The young man laughed at my discomfiture.

'Mad dog,' he said. 'All the dogs are going mad. Biting people. Running all over the place and biting people. We have to round them up.'

'And then what will you do? Shoot them?'

'Not allowed to kill them. Cruelty to animals.'

'So then?'

'We'll let them loose in the jungle—down near Rajpur.'

'But they'll start biting people there.'

'Problem for Rajpur.' He smiled disarmingly—canines like a wolf's.

'If they are mad they'll die anyway,' I said. 'But don't you have a vet—an animal doctor—in this place?'

'Not in Fosterganj. Only in Rajpur. That's why we leave them there.'

Defeated by this logic, I picked up my two suitcases and crossed the empty street to Hassan's bakery. The taxi sped away; no business in Fosterganj.

∽

Over the next few days, several people were bitten and had to go down to Dehra for anti-rabies treatment. The cobbler's wife refused to go, and was dead within the month. There were many cases in Rajpur, due no doubt to the sudden influx of mad dogs expelled from Fosterganj.

In due course, life returned to normal, as it always does in India, post earthquakes, cyclones, riots, epidemics, and cricket controversies. Apathy, or lethargy, or a combination of the two, soon casts a spell over everything and the most traumatic events are quickly forgotten.

'Sab chalta hai,' Hassan, my philosophical landlord, would say, speaking for everyone.

It did not take me long to settle down in my little

room above the bakery. Recent showers had brought out the sheen on new leaves, transformed the grass on the hillside from a faded yellow to an emerald green. A barbet atop a spruce tree was in full cry. It would keep up its monotonous chant all summer. And early morning, a whistling-thrush would render its interrupted melody, never quite finishing what it had to say.

It was good to hear the birds and laughing schoolchildren through my open window. But I soon learnt to shut it whenever I went out. Late one morning, on returning from my walk, I found a large rhesus monkey sitting on my bed, tearing up a loaf of bread that Hassan had baked for me. I tried to drive the fellow away, but he seemed reluctant to leave. He bared his teeth and swore at me in monkey language. Then he stuffed a piece of bread into his mouth and glared at me, daring me to do my worst. I recalled that monkeys carry rabies, and not wanting to join those who had recently been bitten by rabid dogs, I backed out of the room and called for help. One of Hassan's brood came running up the steps with a hockey stick, and chased the invader away.

'Always keep a mug of water handy,' he told me. 'Throw the water on him and he'll be off. They hate cold water.'

'You may be right,' I said. 'I've never seen a monkey taking a bath.'

'See how miserable they are when it rains,' said my rescuer. 'They huddle together as though it's the end of the world.'

'Strange, isn't it? Birds like bathing in the rain.'

'So do I. Wait till the monsoon comes. You can join me then.'

'Perhaps I will.'

On this friendly note we parted, and I cleaned up the mess made by my simian visitor, and then settled down to do some writing.

But there was something about the atmosphere of Fosterganj that discouraged any kind of serious work or effort. Tucked away in a fold of the hills, its inhabitants had begun to resemble their surroundings: one old man resembled a willow bent by rain and wind; an elderly lady with her umbrella reminded me of a colourful mushroom, quite possibly poisonous; my good baker-cum-landlord looked like a bit of the hillside, scarred and uneven but stable. The children were like young grass, coming up all over the place; but the adolescents were like nettles, you never knew if they would sting when touched. There was a young Tibetan lady whose smile was like the blue sky opening up. And there was no brighter blue than the sky as seen from Fosterganj on a clear day.

It took me some time to get to know all the inhabitants. But one of the first was Professor Lulla, recently retired, who came hurrying down the road like the White Rabbit in *Alice in Wonderland*, glancing at his watch and muttering to himself. If, like the White Rabbit, he was saying 'I'm late, I'm late!' I wouldn't have been at all surprised. I was standing outside the bakery, chatting to one of the children, when he came up to me, adjusted his spectacles, peered at me through murky lenses, and said, 'Welcome to Fosterganj, sir. I believe you've come to stay for the season.'

'I'm not sure how long I'll stay,' I said. 'But thank you for your welcome.'

'We must get together and have a cultural and cultured exchange,' he said, rather pompously. 'Not many intellectuals in Fosterganj, you know.'

'I was hoping there wouldn't be.'

'But we'll talk, we'll talk. Only can't stop now. I have a funeral to attend. Eleven o'clock at the Camel's Back cemetery. Poor woman. Dead. Quite dead. Would you care to join me?'

'Er—I'm not in a party mood,' I said. 'And I don't think I knew the deceased.'

'Old Miss Gamleh. Your landlord thought she was a flowerpot—would have been ninety next month. Wonderful woman. Hated chokra-boys.' He looked distastefully at the boy grinning up at him. 'Stole all her plums, if the monkeys didn't get them first. Spent all her life in the hill station. Never married. Jilted by a weedy British colonel, awful fellow, even made off with her savings. But she managed on her own. Kept poultry, sold eggs to the hotels.'

'What happens to the poultry?' I asked.

'Oh, hens can look after themselves,' he said airily. 'But I can't linger or I'll be late. It's a long walk to the cemetery.'

And he set off in determined fashion, like Scott of the Antarctic about to brave a blizzard.

'Must have been a close friend, the old lady who passed away,' I remarked.

'Not at all,' said Hassan, who had been standing in his doorway listening to the conversation. 'I doubt if she ever spoke to him. But Professor Lulla never misses a funeral. He goes to all of them—cremations, burials—funerals of any well-known person, even strangers. It's a hobby with him.'

'Extraordinary,' I said. 'I thought collecting matchbox labels was sad enough as a hobby. Doesn't it depress him?'

'It seems to cheer him up, actually. But I must go too, sir. If you don't mind keeping an eye on the bakery for an hour or two, I'll hurry along to the funeral and see if I can get her poultry cheap. Miss Gamla's hens give good eggs, I'm told. Little Ali will look after the customers, sir. All you have to do is see that they don't make off with the buns and creamrolls.'

I don't know if Hassan attended the funeral, but he came back with two baskets filled with cackling hens, and a rooster to keep them company.

ENTER A MAN-EATER

Did I say nothing ever happens in Fosterganj?

That is true in many ways. If you don't count the outbreak of rabies, that is, or the annual depredations of a man-eating leopard, or the drownings in the pool.

I suppose I should start with the leopard, since its activities commenced not long after I came to live in Fosterganj.

Its first victim was Professor Lulla, who was on his way to attend another funeral.

I don't remember who had died. But I remember the cremation was to take place in Rajpur, at the bottom of the hill, an hour's walk from Fosterganj. The professor was anxious not to miss it, although he had met the recipient of the honour only once. Before the sun was up, he was on his way down the mountain trail. At that early hour, the mist from the valley rises, and it obscured the view, so that he probably did not see the leopard as it followed silently behind him, waiting its opportunity, stalking its victim with pleasurable anticipation. The importunate professor might have heard the rattle of stones as the leopard charged; might have had a glimpse of it as it sprang at his throat; might even have uttered a cry, or screamed for help. But there was no one to hear, no witness of the attack.

The leopard dragged the dying man into the kingora bushes and began to gnaw at his flesh. He was still at his meal when, half an hour later, a group of Nepali labourers came down the path, singing and making merry, and frightened the beast away. They found the mangled remains of the professor; two of the party ran back to Fosterganj for help, while the rest stood guard over the half-eaten torso.

Help came in the form of half the population of

Fosterganj. There was nothing they could do, as the leopard did not return. But next day they gave the professor a good funeral.

However, a couple of public-spirited citizens were determined to hunt down the leopard before it took a further toll on human life. One of them was our local bank manager, Vishaal, a friendly and amiable sort, who was also a self-confessed disciple of Jim Corbett, the great shikari who had disposed of dozens of man-eaters. Vishaal did not possess a gun, but the bank's chowkidar, a retired Gurkha soldier, did. He had an ancient 12-bore shotgun which he carried about with him wherever he was on duty. The gun hadn't been fired for years—not since it had gone off accidentally when being handled by an inquisitive customer.

Vishaal found a box of cartridges in the bank's safe. They had been there for several years and looked a little mouldy, as did almost everything in Fosterganj, including some of the older residents. 'Stay here more than three years,' philosophized Hassan, 'and unless you have God on your side, your hair goes white and your teeth get yellow. Everyone ends up looking like old Foster— descendent of the kings of Scotland!'

'It must be the water,' I said.

'No, it's the mist,' said Hassan. 'It hangs around Fosterganj even in good weather. It keeps the sun out. Look at my bread. Can't keep a loaf fresh for more than a day, the mould gets to it in no time. And the monsoon hasn't even begun!'

In spite of his bad teeth and ragged appearance, however, Foster—or Bonnie Prince Charlie, as the older residents called him—was fairly active, and it was he who set up a rough machaan in an old oak tree overlooking the stream at the bottom of the hill. He even sold Vishaal an old goat, to be used as bait for the leopard.

Vishaal persuaded me to keep him company on the machaan, and produced a bottle of brandy that he said would see us through the night.

Our vigil began at eight, and by midnight the brandy bottle was empty. No leopard, although the goat made its presence apparent by bleating without a break.

'If the leopard has developed a taste for humans,' I said, 'why should it come for a silly old goat?'

I dozed off for some time, only to be awakened by a nudge from Vishaal, who whispered, 'Something's out there. I think it's the leopard! Shine the torch on it!'

I shone the torch on the terrified goat, and at the same moment a leopard sprang out of the bushes and seized its victim. There was a click from Vishaal's gun. The cartridge had failed to go off.

'Fire the other barrel!' I urged.

The second cartridge went off. There was a tremendous bang. But by then both leopard and goat had vanished into the night.

'I thought you said it only liked humans,' said Vishaal.

'Must be another leopard,' I said.

We trudged back to his rooms, and opened another bottle of brandy.

In the morning a villager came to the bank and demanded a hundred rupees for his goat.

'But it was Foster's goat,' protested Vishaal. 'I've already paid him for it.'

'Not Foster Sahib's goat,' said the villager. 'He only borrowed it for the night.'

A MAGIC OIL

A day or two later I was in the bank, run by Vishaal (manager), Negi (cashier), and Suresh (peon). I was sitting opposite Vishaal, who was at his desk, taken up by two handsome paperweights but no papers. Suresh had brought me a cup of tea from the tea shop across the road. There was just one customer in the bank, Hassan, who was making a deposit. A cosy summer morning in Fosterganj: not much happening, but life going on just the same.

In walked Foster. He'd made an attempt at shaving, but appeared to have given up at a crucial stage, because now he looked like a wasted cricketer finally on his way out. The effect was enhanced by the fact that he was wearing flannel trousers that had once been white but were now greenish yellow; the previous monsoon was to blame. He had found an old tie, and this was strung round his neck, or rather his unbuttoned shirt collar. The said shirt had seen many summers and winters in Fosterganj, and was frayed at the cuffs. Even so, Foster looked quite spry, as compared to when I had last seen him.

'Come in, come in!' said Vishaal, always polite to his customers, even those who had no savings. 'How is your gladioli farm?'

'Coming up nicely,' said Foster. 'I'm growing potatoes too.'

'Very nice. But watch out for the porcupines, they love potatoes.'

'Shot one last night. Cut my hands getting the quills out. But porcupine meat is great. I'll send you some the next time I shoot one.'

'Well, keep some ammunition for the leopard. We've got to get it before it kills someone else.'

'It won't be around for two or three weeks. They keep moving, do leopards. He'll circle the mountain, then be back in these parts. But that's not what I came to see you about, Mr Vishaal. I was hoping for a small loan.'

'Small loan, big loan, that's what we are here for. In what way can we help you, sir?'

'I want to start a chicken farm.'

'Most original.'

'There's a great shortage of eggs in Mussoorie. The hotels want eggs, the schools want eggs, the restaurants want eggs. And they have to get them from Rajpur or Dehradun.'

'Hassan has a few hens,' I put in.

'Only enough for home consumption. I'm thinking in terms of hundreds of eggs—and broiler chickens for the table. I want to make Fosterganj the chicken capital of India. It will be like old times, when my ancestor planted the first potatoes here, brought all the way from Scotland!'

'I thought they came from Ireland,' I said. 'Captain Young, up at Landour.'

'Oh well, we brought other things. Like Scotch whisky.'

'Actually, Irish whisky got here first. Captain Kennedy, up in Simla.' I wasn't Irish, but I was in a combative frame of mind, which is the same as being Irish.

To mollify Foster, I said, 'You did bring the bagpipe.' And when he perked up, I added: 'But the Gurkha is better at playing it.'

This contretemps over, Vishaal got Foster to sign a couple of forms and told him that the loan would be processed in due course and that we'd all celebrate over a bottle of Scotch whisky. Foster left the room with something of a swagger. The prospect of some money coming in—even if it is someone else's—will put any man in an optimistic frame of mind. And for Foster the prospect of losing it was as yet far distant.

I wanted to make a phone call to my bank in Delhi, so that I could have some of my savings sent to me, and Vishaal kindly allowed me to use his phone.

There were only four phones in all of Fosterganj, and there didn't seem to be any necessity for more. The bank had one. So did Dr Bisht. So did Brigadier Bakshi, retired. And there was one in the police station, but it was usually out of order.

The police station, a one-room affair, was manned

by a Daroga and a constable. If the Daroga felt like a nap, the constable took charge. And if the constable took the afternoon off, the Daroga would run the place. This worked quite well, as there wasn't much crime in Fosterganj—if you didn't count Foster's illicit still at the bottom of the hill (Scottish hooch, he called the stuff he distilled); or a charming young delinquent called Sunil, who picked pockets for a living (though not in Fosterganj); or the barber who supplemented his income by supplying charas to his agents at some of the boarding schools; or the man who sold the secretions of certain lizards, said to increase sexual potency—except that it was only linseed oil, used for oiling cricket bats.

I found the last mentioned, a man called Rattan Lal, sitting on a stool outside my door when I returned from the bank.

'Saande-ka-tel,' he declared abruptly, holding up a small bottle containing a vitreous yellow fluid. 'Just one application, sahib, and the size and strength of your valuable member will increase dramatically. It will break down doors, should doors be shut against you. No chains will hold it down. You will be as a stallion, rampant in a field full of fillies. Sahib, you will rule the roost! Memsahibs and beautiful women will fall at your feet.'

'It will get me into trouble, for certain,' I demurred. 'It's great stuff, I'm sure. But wasted here in Fosterganj.'

Rattan Lal would not be deterred. 'Sahib, every time you try it, you will notice an increase in dimensions, guaranteed!'

'Like Pinocchio's nose,' I said in English. He looked puzzled. He understood the word 'nose', but had no idea what I meant.

'Naak?' he said. 'No, sahib, you don't rub it on your nose. Here, down between the legs,' and he made as if to give a demonstration. I held a hand up to restrain him.

'There was a boy named Pinocchio in a far-off country,' I explained, switching back to Hindi. 'His nose grew longer every time he told a lie.'

'I tell no lies, sahib. Look, my nose is normal. Rest is very big. You want to see?'

'Another day,' I said.

'Only ten rupees.'

'The bottle or the rest of you?'

'You joke, sahib,' and he thrust a bottle into my unwilling hands and removed a ten-rupee note from my shirt pocket; all done very simply.

'I will come after a month and check up,' he said. 'Next time I will bring the saanda itself! You are in the prime of your life, it will make you a bull among men.' And away he went.

The little bottle of oil stood unopened on the bathroom shelf for weeks. I was too scared to use it. It was like the bottle in *Alice in Wonderland* with the label DRINK ME. Alice drank it, and shot up to the ceiling. I wasn't sure I wanted to grow that high.

I did wonder what would happen if I applied some of it to my scalp. Would it stimulate hair growth? Would it stimulate my thought processes? Put an end to writer's block?

Well, I never did find out. One afternoon I heard a clatter in the bathroom and looked in to see a large and sheepish-looking monkey jump out of the window with the bottle.

But to return to Rattan Lal—some hours after I had been sold the aphrodisiac, I was walking up to town to get a newspaper when I met him on his way down.

'Any luck with the magic oil?' I asked.

'All sold out!' he said, beaming with pleasure. 'Ten bottles sold at the Savoy, and six at Hakman's. What a night it's going to be for them.' And he rubbed his hands at the prospect.

'A very busy night,' I said. 'Either that, or they'll be looking for you to get their money back.'

'I come next month. If you are still here, I'll keep another bottle for you. Look there!' He took me by the arm and pointed at a large rock lizard that was sunning itself on the parapet. 'You catch me some of those, and I'll pay you for them. Be my partner. Bring me lizards—not small ones, only big fellows—and I will buy!'

'How do you extract the tel?' I asked.

'Ah, that's a trade secret. But I will show you when you bring me some saandas. Now I must go. My good wife waits for me with impatience.'

And off he went, down the bridle path to Rajpur.

The rock lizard was still on the wall, enjoying its afternoon siesta.

It did occur to me that I might make a living from breeding rock lizards. Perhaps Vishaal would give me a loan. I wasn't making much as a writer.

FAIRY GLEN PALACE

The old bridle path from Rajpur to Mussoorie passed through Fosterganj at a height of about five thousand feet. In the old days, before the motor road was built, this was the only road to the hill station. You could ride up on a pony, or walk, or be carried in a basket (if you were a child) or in a doolie (if you were a lady or an invalid). The doolie was a cross between a hammock, a stretcher and a sedan chair, if you can imagine such a contraption. It was borne aloft by two perspiring partners. Sometimes they sat down to rest, and dropped you unceremoniously. I have a picture of my grandmother being borne uphill in a doolie, and she looks petrified. There was an incident in which a doolie, its occupant and two bearers, all went over a cliff just before Fosterganj, and perished in the fall.

Sometimes you can see the ghost of this poor lady being borne uphill by two phantom bearers.

Fosterganj has its ghosts, of course. And they are something of a distraction.

Writing is my vocation, and I have always tried to follow the apostolic maxim: 'Study to be quiet and to mind your own business.' But in small-town India one is constantly drawn into other people's business, just as they are drawn towards yours. In Fosterganj it was quiet enough, there were few people; there was no excuse for shirking work. But tales of haunted houses and fairy-infested forests have always intrigued me, and when I heard that the ruined palace halfway down to Rajpur was a place to be avoided after dark, it was natural for me to start taking my evening walks in its direction.

Fairy Glen was its name. It had been built on the lines of a Swiss or French chalet, with numerous turrets decorating its many wings—a huge, rambling building, two-storeyed, with numerous balconies and cornices and windows; a hodge-podge of architectural styles, a wedding cake of a palace, built to satisfy the whims and fancies of its late owner, the Raja of Ranipur, a small state near the Nepal border. Maintaining this ornate edifice must have been something of a nightmare; and the present heirs had quite given up on it, for bits of the roof were missing, some windows were without panes, doors had developed cracks, and what had once been a garden was now a small jungle. Apparently there was no one living there any more; no sign of a caretaker. I had walked past the wrought-iron gate several times without seeing any signs of life, apart from a large grey cat sunning itself outside a broken window.

Then one evening, walking up from Rajpur, I was caught in a storm.

A wind had sprung up, bringing with it dark,

overburdened clouds. Heavy drops of rain were followed by hailstones bouncing off the stony path. Gusts of wind rushed through the oaks, and leaves and small branches were soon swirling through the air. I was still a couple of miles from the Fosterganj bazaar, and I did not fancy sheltering under a tree, as flashes of lightning were beginning to light up the darkening sky. Then I found myself outside the gate of the abandoned palace.

Outside the gate stood an old sentry box. No one had stood sentry in it for years. It was a good place in which to shelter. But I hesitated because a large bird was perched on the gate, seemingly oblivious to the rain that was still falling.

It looked like a crow or a raven, but it was much bigger than either—in fact, twice the size of a crow, but having all the features of one—and when a flash of lightning lit up the gate, it gave a squawk, opened its enormous wings and took off, flying in the direction of the oak forest. I hadn't seen such a bird before; there was something dark and malevolent and almost supernatural about it. But it had gone, and I darted into the sentry box without further delay.

I had been standing there some ten minutes, wondering when the rain was going to stop, when I heard someone running down the road. As he approached, I could see that he was just a boy, probably eleven or twelve; but in the dark I could not make out his features. He came up to the gate, lifted the latch, and was about to go in when he saw me in the sentry box.

'Kaun? Who are you?' he asked, first in Hindi then in English. He did not appear to be in any way anxious or alarmed.

'Just sheltering from the rain,' I said. 'I live in the bazaar.' He took a small torch from his pocket and shone it in my face.

'Yes, I have seen you there. A tourist.'

'A writer. I stay in places, I don't just pass through.'

'Do you want to come in?'

I hesitated. It was still raining and the roof of the sentry box was leaking badly.

'Do you live here?' I asked.

'Yes, I am the raja's nephew. I live here with my mother. Come in.' He took me by the hand and led me through the gate. His hand was quite rough and heavy for an eleven- or twelve-year-old. Instead of walking with me to the front steps and entrance of the old palace, he led me around to the rear of the building, where a faint light glowed in a mullioned window, and in its light I saw that he had a very fresh and pleasant face—a face as yet untouched by the trials of life.

Instead of knocking on the door, he tapped on the window.

'Only strangers knock on the door,' he said. 'When I tap on the window, my mother knows it's me.'

'That's clever of you,' I said.

He tapped again, and the door was opened by an unusually tall woman wearing a kind of loose, flowing gown that looked strange in that place, and on her. The light was behind her, and I couldn't see her face until we had entered the room. When she turned to me, I saw that she had a long reddish scar running down one side of her face. Even so, there was a certain, hard beauty in her appearance.

'Make some tea—Mother,' said the boy rather brusquely.

'And something to eat. I'm hungry. Sir, will you have something?' He looked enquiringly at me. The light from a kerosene lamp fell full on his face. He was wide-eyed, full-lipped, smiling; only his voice seemed rather mature for one so young. And he spoke like someone much older, with an almost unsettling sophistication.

'Sit down, sir.' He led me to a chair, made me comfortable. 'You are not too wet, I hope?'

'No, I took shelter before the rain came down too heavily. But you are wet, you'd better change.'

'It doesn't bother me.' And after a pause, 'Sorry there is no electricity. Bills haven't been paid for years.'

'Is this your place?'

'No, we are only caretakers. Poor relations, you might say. The palace has been in dispute for many years. The raja and his brothers keep fighting over it, and meanwhile it is slowly falling apart. The lawyers are happy. Perhaps I should study and become a lawyer some day.'

'Do you go to school?'

'Sometimes.'

'How old are you?'

'Quite old, I'm not sure. Mother, how old am I?' he asked, as the tall woman returned with cups of tea and a plateful of biscuits.

She hesitated, gave him a puzzled look. 'Don't you know? It's on your certificate.'

'I've lost the certificate.'

'No, I've kept it safely.' She looked at him intently, placed a hand on his shoulder, then turned to me and said, 'He is twelve,' with a certain finality.

We finished our tea. It was still raining.

'It will rain all night,' said the boy. 'You had better stay here.'

'It will inconvenience you.'

'No, it won't. There are many rooms. If you do not mind the darkness. Come, I will show you everything. And meanwhile my mother will make some dinner. Very simple food, I hope you won't mind.'

The boy took me around the old palace, if you could still call it that. He led the way with a candleholder from which a large candle threw our exaggerated shadows on the walls.

'What's your name?' I asked, as he led me into what must have been a reception room, still crowded with ornate furniture and bric-a-brac.

'Bhim,' he said. 'But everyone calls me Lucky.'

'And are you lucky?'

He shrugged. 'Don't know....' Then he smiled up at me. 'Maybe you'll bring me luck.'

We walked further into the room. Large oil paintings

hung from the walls, gathering mould. Some were portraits of royalty, kings and queens of another era, wearing decorative headgear, strange uniforms, the women wrapped in jewellery—more jewels than garments, it seemed—and sometimes accompanied by children who were also weighed down by excessive clothing. A young man sat on a throne, his lips curled in a sardonic smile.

'My grandfather,' said Bhim.

He led me into a large bedroom taken up by a four-poster bed which had probably seen several royal couples copulating upon it. It looked cold and uninviting, but Bhim produced a voluminous razai from a cupboard and assured me that it would be warm and quite luxurious, as it had been his grandfather's.

'And when did your grandfather die?' I asked.

'Oh, fifty-sixty years ago, it must have been.'

'In this bed, I suppose.'

'No, he was shot accidentally while out hunting. They said it was an accident. But he had enemies.'

'Kings have enemies.... And this was the royal bed?'

He gave me a sly smile; not so innocent after all. 'Many women slept in it. He had many queens.'

'And concubines.'

'What are concubines?'

'Unofficial queens.'

'Yes, those too.'

A worldly-wise boy of twelve.

A BIG BLACK BIRD

I did not feel like sleeping in that room, with its musty old draperies and paint peeling off the walls. A trickle of water from the ceiling fell down the back of my shirt and made me shiver.

'The roof is leaking,' I said. 'Maybe I'd better go home.'

'You can't go now, it's very late. And that leopard has been seen again.'

He fetched a china bowl from the dressing table and placed it on the floor to catch the trickle from the ceiling. In another corner of the room a metal bucket was receiving a steady patter from another leak.

'The palace is leaking everywhere,' said Bhim cheerfully. 'This is the only dry room.'

He took me by the hand and led me back to his own quarters. I was surprised, again, by how heavy and rough his hand was for a boy, and presumed that he did a certain amount of manual work such as chopping wood for a daily fire. In winter the building would be unbearably cold.

His mother gave us a satisfying meal, considering the ingredients at her disposal were somewhat limited. Once again, I tried to get away. But only half-heartedly. The boy intrigued me; so did his mother; so did the rambling old palace; and the rain persisted.

Bhim the Lucky took me to my room; waited with the guttering candle till I had removed my shoes; handed me a pair of very large pyjamas.

'Royal pyjamas,' he said with a smile.

I got into them and floated around.

'Before you go—' I said. 'I might want to visit the bathroom in the night.'

'Of course, sir. It's close by.' He opened a door, and beyond it I saw a dark passage. 'Go a little way, and there's a door on the left. I'm leaving an extra candle and matches on the dressing table.'

He put the lighted candle he was carrying on the table, and left the room without a light. Obviously he knew his way about in the dark. His footsteps receded, and I was left alone with the sound of raindrops pattering on the roof and a loose sheet of corrugated tin roofing flapping away in a wind that had now sprung up.

It was a summer's night, and I had no need of blankets; so I removed my shoes and jacket and lay down on the capacious bed, wondering if I should blow the candle out or allow it to burn as long as it lasted.

Had I been in my own room, I would have been reading—a Conrad or a Chekhov or some other classic—because at night I turn to the classics—but here there was no light and nothing to read.

I got up and blew the candle out. I might need it later on.

Restless, I prowled around the room in the dark, banging into chairs and footstools. I made my way to the window and drew the curtains aside. Some light filtered into the room because behind the clouds there was a moon, and it had been a full moon the night before.

I lay back on the bed. It wasn't very comfortable. It was a box-bed, of the sort that had only just begun to become popular in households with small bedrooms. This one had been around for some time—no doubt a very early version of its type—and although it was covered with a couple of thick mattresses, the woodwork appeared to have warped because it creaked loudly whenever I shifted my position. The boards no longer fitted properly. Either that, or the box-bed had been overstuffed with all sorts of things.

After some time I settled into one position and dozed off for a while, only to be awakened by the sound of someone screaming somewhere in the building. My hair stood on end. The screaming continued, and I wondered if I should get up to investigate. Then suddenly it stopped—broke off in the middle as though it had been muffled by a hand or piece of cloth.

There was a tapping at the pane of the big French window in front of the bed. Probably the branch of a tree, swaying in the wind. But then there was a screech, and I sat up in bed. Another screech, and I was out of it.

I went to the window and pressed my face to the glass. The big black bird—the bird I had seen when taking shelter in the sentry box—was sitting, or rather squatting, on the boundary wall, facing me. The moon, now visible through the clouds, fell full upon it. I had never seen a bird like it before. Crow-like, but heavily built, like a turkey, its beak that of a bird of prey, its talons those of a vulture. I stepped back, and closed the heavy curtains, shutting out the light but also shutting out the image of that menacing bird.

Returning to the bed, I just sat there for a while, wondering if I should get up and leave. The rain had lessened. But the luminous dial of my watch showed it was two in the morning. No time for a stroll in the dark—not with a man-eating leopard in the vicinity.

Then I heard the shriek again. It seemed to echo through the building. It may have been the bird, but to me it sounded all too human. There was silence for a long while after that. I lay back on the bed and tried to sleep. But it was even more uncomfortable than before. Perhaps the wood had warped too much during the monsoon, I thought, and the lid of the old box-bed did not fit properly. Maybe I could push it back into its correct position; then perhaps I could get some sleep.

So I got up again, and after fumbling around in the dark for a few minutes, found the matches and lit the candle. Then I removed the sheets from the bed and pulled away the two mattresses. The cover of the box-bed lay exposed. And a hand protruded from beneath the lid.

It was not a living hand. It was a skeletal hand, fleshless, brittle. But there was a ring on one finger, an opal still clinging to the bone of a small index finger. It glowed faintly in the candlelight.

Shaking a little (for I am really something of a coward, though an inquisitive one), I lifted the lid of the box-bed. Laid out on a pretty counterpane was a skeleton.

A bundle of bones, but still clothed in expensive-looking garments. One hand gripped the side of the box-bed; the hand that had kept it from shutting properly.

I dropped the lid of the box-bed and ran from the room—only to blunder into a locked door. Someone, presumably the boy, had locked me into the bedroom.

I banged on the door and shouted, but no one heard me. No one came running. I went to the large French window, but it was firmly fastened, it probably hadn't been opened for many years.

Then I remembered the passageway leading to the bathroom. The boy had pointed it out to me. Possibly there was a way out from there.

There was. It was an old door that opened easily, and I stepped out into the darkness, finding myself entangled in a creeper that grew against the wall. From its cloying fragrance I recognized it as wisteria.

A narrow path led to a wicket-gate at the end of the building. I found my way out of the grounds and back on the familiar public road. The old palace loomed out of the darkness. I turned my back on it and set off for home, my little room above Hassan's bakery.

Nothing happens in Fosterganj, I told myself. But something had happened in that old palace.

THE STREET OF LOST HOMES

'What did you want to go there for?' asked Hassan, when I knocked on his door at the crack of dawn.

'It was raining heavily, and I stopped near the gate to take shelter. A boy invited me in, his mother gave me something to eat, and I ended up spending the night in the raja's bedroom.' I said nothing about screams in the night or the skeleton in the bed.

Hassan presented me with a bun and a glass of hot sweet tea.

'Nobody goes there,' he said. 'The place has a bad name.'

'And why's that?'

'The old raja was a bad man. Tortured his wives, or so it was said.'

'And what happened to him?'

'Got killed in a hunting accident, in the jungles next to Bijnor. He went after a tiger, but the tiger got to him first. Bit his head off! Everyone was pleased. His younger brother inherited the palace, but he never comes here. I think he still lives somewhere near the Nepal border.'

'And the people who still live in the palace?'

'Poor relations, I think. Offspring from one of the raja's wives or concubines—no one quite knows, or even cares. We don't see much of them, and they keep to themselves. But people avoid the place, they say it is still full of evil, haunted by the old scoundrel whose cruelty has left its mark on the walls.... It should be pulled down!'

'It's falling down of its own accord,' I said. 'Most of it is already a ruin.'

Later that morning I found Hassan closing the doors of the bakery.

'Are you off somewhere?' I asked.

He nodded. 'Down to Rajpur. My boys are at school and my daughter is too small to look after the place.'

'It's urgent, then?'

'That fool of a youth, Sunil, has got into trouble. Picking someone's pocket, no doubt. They are holding him at the Rajpur thana.

'But why do you have to go? Doesn't he have any relatives?'

'None of any use. His father died some time back. He did me a favour once. More than a favour—he saved my life. So I must help the boy, even if he is a badmash.'

'I'll come with you,' I said on an impulse. 'Is it very far?'

'Rajpur is at the bottom of the hill. About an hour's walk down the footpath. Quicker than walking up to Mussoorie and waiting for a bus.'

I joined him on the road, and together we set off down the old path.

We passed Fairy Glen—the ruin where I had passed the night. It looked quite peaceful in the April sunshine. The gate was closed. There was no sign of the boy or his mother, my hosts of the previous night. It would have been embarrassing to meet them, for I had left in an almighty hurry. There was no sign of the big black bird, either. Only a couple of mynahs squabbling on the wall, and a black-faced langur swinging from the branch of an oak.

I had some difficulty in keeping up with Hassan. Although he was over forty and had the beginnings of a paunch, he was a sturdy fellow, and he had the confident, even stride of someone who had spent most of his life in the hills.

The path was a steep one, and it began to level out only when it entered the foothills hamlet of Rajpur. At that time Rajpur was something of a ghost town. Some sixteen years earlier, most of its inhabitants, Muslims like Hassan, had fled or been killed by mobs during the communal strife that followed the partition of the country.

Rajpur had yet to recover. We passed empty, gutted buildings, some roofless, some without doors and windows. Weeds and small bushes grew out of the floors of abandoned houses. Successive monsoons had removed the mud or cement plaster from the walls, leaving behind bare brickwork which was beginning to crumble. The entire length of the street, where once there had been a hundred homes pulsating with life and human endeavour, now stood empty, homes only to jackals, snakes, and huge rock lizards.

Hassan stopped before an empty doorway. Behind it an empty courtyard. Behind it a wall with empty windows.

'I lived here once,' he said. 'My parents, younger brother, sister, my first wife...all of us worked together, making bread and buns and pastries for the rich folk in the houses along the Dehra road. And in one night I lost everyone, everything—parents, brother, sister, wife.... The fire swept through the mohalla, and those who ran out of their houses were cut down by swords and kirpans.'

I stopped and put a hand on his shoulder.

'It's hard for me to talk about it. Later, perhaps....' And he moved on.

The street of lost homes gave way to a small bazaar, the only visible sign of some sort of recovery. A young man from a nearby village ran the small dhaba where we stopped for tea and pakoras. He was too young to have any memories of 1947. And in India, town and countryside often appear to have completely different histories.

Hassan asked me to wait at the dhaba while he walked down to the local thana to enquire after Sunil.

'A thana is no place for a respectable person like you,' he said.

'In Delhi, the prisons are full of respectable people,' I said.

'But not respected anymore?'

'Well, some of them don't seem to be too bothered. They get bail, come out with a swagger, and drive home in their cars.'

'And what are their crimes?'

'The same as Sunil's. They pick pockets, but in a big way. You don't see them doing it. But carry on, I'll wait here for you.'

The dhak, or flame of the forest, was in flower, and I sat on a bench taking in the sights and sounds of summer's arrival in the valley. Scarlet bougainvillea cascaded over a low wall, and a flock of parrots flung themselves from one tall mango tree to another, sampling the young unripe fruit.

'Will there be a good crop this year?' I asked the young dhabawala.

'Should be, if the parrots and monkeys leave any for us.'

'You need a chowkidar,' I said, and thought of recommending Sunil. But Hassan came back without him.

'No magistrate in court today. We'll try again tomorrow.

In the meantime he gets board and lodging at government expense. He doesn't have to pick any pockets.'

'He will, if he gets a chance. It's an incurable disease.'

EYE OF THE LEOPARD

We did not return by way of the ruined and deserted township. Hassan wished to avoid it. 'Bad memories,' he said.

We cut across a couple of fields until we reached a small stream which came down the ravine below Fosterganj. Hassan knew it well. He went there to bathe from time to time. A narrow path took us upstream.

'How did you escape?' I asked, still curious about the events of 1947.

Hassan continued to walk, looking straight ahead. He did not turn his face to me as he spoke. 'I was late returning from Mussoorie. The houses were already ablaze. I began running towards ours, but the mob cut me off. Most of them Sikhs, wanting revenge—they had lost homes and loved ones in the Punjab—there was madness everywhere—hate and greed and madness. Gandhi couldn't stop it. Several men caught hold of me and flung me to the ground. One stood over me with his sword raised. That's when Bhai Saheb—Sunil's father— appeared as if out of nowhere. "What are you doing?" he cried. "That's my nephew. Don't touch him, or my entire village will be up in arms against you!" The attackers left me and moved on to other targets. Of course it was all over with my people. Sunil's father kept me in his village, not far from here, until the killing stopped. Sooner or later it had to stop. It exhausts itself. A few hours of madness and we spend years counting the cost.'

After almost an hour of walking upstream, slipping on moss-covered boulders and struggling up the little-used pathway, we came to a pool, a catchment area where the water was still and deep.

'We'll rest here awhile,' said Hassan. 'Would you like to bathe?'

It was a warm day, and down there in the ravine there was no breeze. I stripped to my underwear and slipped into the pool.

After some time Hassan joined me. He was a well-built man. Birthing and raising so many children had worn out his consumptive wife, but he was in fine shape—strong in the chest and thighs; he had the build of a wrestler.

I was enjoying the water, swimming around, but Hassan was restless, continually looking up at the hillside and the overhanging branches of the trees that grew near the water. Presently he left the pool and began striding up a grassy knoll as though in search of something—as though he sensed the presence of danger. If you have faced danger once, you will know when it comes again.

'What are you looking for?' I called.

'Nothing,' he replied. 'Just looking around.' And he went further up the path.

I swam around a little, then pulled myself up on a flat boulder, and sat there in the sun, contemplating a thicket of ferns. A long-tailed magpie squawked and flew away in a hurry. The sun was in my eyes. I turned my back to it, and looked up into the yellow eyes of a leopard crouching on the rocks above me.

I wanted to shout, but couldn't. And perhaps it was better that I remained silent. Was it the man-eater? There was no way of knowing, but it seemed likely.

For what seemed an age, I looked at the leopard and the leopard stared at me. In fact, it was only a matter of seconds; but each second was an hour to me.

The leopard came forward a little and snarled. Perhaps he was puzzled that I made no sound and did not run. But he sank down, his forepaws spreading to get a grip on the rocks. His tail began to twitch—a sure signal that he was about to spring. His lips drew back and the sun shone on his canines and the dark pink of his gums.

Then I saw Hassan appear just behind the crouching beast. He held a large rock in his hands—it was bigger than a football. He raised his arms and brought the rock down with all his might on the leopard's head.

The leopard seemed to sag. Its paws scrabbled in the dust. Blood trickled from its ears. Hassan appeared again, with an even bigger rock, and he brought it down with such force that I heard the animal's skull crack. There was a convulsive movement, and then it was still.

ॐ

We returned to Fosterganj and told everyone that the man-eater was dead. A number of people went down to the stream to fetch the carcass. But Hassan did not join them. He was behind with his work, and had to bake twenty to thirty loaves of bread for delivery the next morning. I tried to help him, but I am not much good at baking bread, and he told me to go to bed early.

Everyone was pleased that the leopard had been killed.

Everyone, that is, except Vishaal, the bank manager, who had been hoping to vanquish it himself.

AN EVENING WITH FOSTER

Keep right on to the end of the road,
Keep right on to the end.
If your way be long
Let your heart be strong,
And keep right on to the end.
If you're tired and weary
Still carry on,
Till you come to your happy abode.
And then all you love
And are dreaming of,
Will be there—
At the end of the road!

The voice of Sir Harry Lauder, Scottish troubadour of the 1930s, singing one of his favourites, came drifting across the hillside as I took the winding path to Foster's cottage.

On one of my morning walks, I had helped him round up some runaway hens, and he had been suitably grateful.

'Ah, it's a fowl subject, trying to run a poultry farm,' he quipped. 'I've already lost a few to jackals and foxes. Hard to keep them in their pens. They jump over the netting and wander all over the place. But thank you for your help. It's good to be young. Once the knees go, you'll never be young again. Why don't you come over in the evening and split a bottle with me? It's a home-made brew, can't hurt you.'

I'd heard of Foster's home-made brew. More than one person had tumbled down the khad after partaking of the stuff. But I did not want to appear standoffish, and besides, I was curious about the man and his history. So towards sunset one summer's evening, I took the path down to his cottage, following the strains of Harry Lauder.

The music grew louder as I approached, and I had to knock on the door several times before it was opened by my bleary-eyed host. He had already been at the stuff he drank, and at first he failed to recognize me.

'Nice old song you have there,' I said. 'My father used to sing it when I was a boy.'

Recognition dawned, and he invited me in. 'Come in, laddie, come in. I've been expecting you. Have a seat!'

The seat he referred to was an old sofa and it was occupied by three cackling hens. With a magnificent sweep of the arm Foster swept them away, and they joined two other hens and a cock-bird on a book rack at the other end of the room. I made sure there were no droppings on the sofa before subsiding into it.

'Birds are finding it too hot out in the yard,' he explained. 'Keep wanting to come indoors.'

The gramophone record had run its course, and Foster switched off the old record player.

'Used to have a real gramophone,' he said, 'but can't

get the needles any more. These electric players aren't any good. But I still have all the old records.' He indicated a pile of 78 rpm gramophone records, and I stretched across and sifted through some of them. Gracie Fields, George Formby, The Street Singer...music hall favourites from the 1930s and 40s. Foster hadn't added to his collection for twenty years.

He must have been close to eighty, almost twice my age. Like his stubble (a permanent feature), the few wisps of hair on his sunburnt head were also grey. Mud had dried on his hands. His old patched-up trousers were held up by braces. There were buttons missing from his shirt, laces missing from his shoes.

'What will you have to drink, laddie? Tea, cocoa, or whisky?'

'Er—not cocoa. Tea, maybe—oh, anything will do.'

'That's the spirit. Go for what you like. I make my own whisky, of course. Real Scotch from the Himalaya. I get the best barley from yonder village.' He gestured towards the next mountain, then turned to a sagging mantelpiece, fetched a bottle that contained an oily yellow liquid, and poured a generous amount into a cracked china mug. He poured a similar amount into a dirty glass tumbler, handed it to me, and said, 'Cheers! Bottoms up!'

'Bottoms up!' I said, and took a gulp.

It wasn't bad. I drank some more and asked Foster how the poultry farm was doing.

'Well, I had fifty birds to start with. But they keep wandering off, and the boys from the village make off with them. I'm down to forty. Sold a few eggs, though. Gave the bank manager the first lot. He seemed pleased. Would you like a few eggs? There's a couple on that cushion, newly laid.'

The said cushion was on a stool a few feet from me. Two large hens' eggs were supported upon it.

'Don't sit on 'em,' said Foster, letting out a cackle which was meant to be laughter. 'They might hatch!'

I took another gulp of Foster's whisky and considered the eggs again. They looked much larger now, more like goose eggs.

Everything was looking larger.

I emptied the glass and stood up to leave.

'Don't go yet,' said Foster. 'You haven't had a proper drink. And there's dinner to follow. Sausages and mash! I make my own sausages, did you know? My sausages were famous all over Mussoorie. I supplied the Savoy, Hakman's, the schools.'

'Why did you stop?' I was back on the sofa, holding another glass of Himalayan Scotch.

'Somebody started spreading a nasty rumour that I was using dog's meat. Now why would I do that when pork was cheap? Of course, during the war years a lot of rubbish went into sausages—stuff you'd normally throw away. That's why they were called "sweet mysteries". You remember the old song? "Ah! Sweet Mystery of Life!" Nebon Eddy and Jeanette Macdonald. Well, the troops used to sing it whenever they were given sausages for breakfast. You never knew what went into them—cats, dogs, camels, scorpions. If you survived those sausages, you survived the war!'

'And *your* sausages, what goes into them?'

'Good, healthy chicken meat. Not crow's meat, as some jealous rivals tried to make out.'

He frowned into his china mug. It was suddenly quieter inside. The hens had joined their sisters in the backyard; they were settling down for the night, sheltering in cardboard cartons and old mango-wood boxes. Quck-quck-quck. Another day nearer to having their sad necks wrung.

I looked around the room. A threadbare carpet. Walls that hadn't received a coat of paint for many years. A couple of loose rafters letting in a blast of cold air. Some pictures here and there—mostly racing scenes. Foster must have been a betting man. Perhaps that was how he ran out of money.

He noticed my interest in the pictures and said, 'Owned a racehorse once. A beauty, she was. That was in Meerut, just before the war. Meerut had a great racecourse. Races every Saturday. Punters came from Delhi. There was money to be made!'

'Did you win any?' I asked.

'Won a couple of races hands down. Then unexpectedly she came in last, and folks lost a lot of money. I had to leave town in a hurry. All my jockey's fault—he was hand in glove with the bookies. They made a killing, of course! Anyway, I sold the horse to a sporting Parsi gentleman and went into the canteen business with my Uncle Fred in Roorkee. That's Uncle Fred, up there.'

Foster gestured towards the mantelpiece. I expected to see a photograph of his Uncle Fred but instead of a photo I found myself staring at a naked skull. It was a well-polished skull and it glistened in the candlelight.

'That's Uncle Fred,' said Foster proudly.

'That skull? Where's the rest of him?'

'In his grave, back in Roorkee.'

'You mean you kept the skull but not the skeleton?'

'Well, it's a long story,' said Foster, 'but to keep it short, Uncle Fred died suddenly of a mysterious malady—a combination of brain fever, blood-pressure, and Housemaid's Knee.'

'Housemaid's Knee!'

'Yes, swollen kneecaps, brought about by being beaten too frequently with police lathis. He wasn't really a criminal, but he'd get into trouble from time to time, harmless little swindles such as printing his own lottery tickets or passing forged banknotes. Spent some time in various district jails until his health broke down. Got a pauper's funeral—but his cadaver was in demand. The students from the local medical college got into the cemetery one night and made off with his cranium! Not that he had much by way of a brain, but he had a handsome, well-formed skull, as you can see.'

I did see. And the skull appeared to be listening to the yarn, because its toothless jaws were extended in a grin; or so I fancied.

'And how did you get it back?' I asked.

'Broke into their demonstration room, naturally. I was younger then, and pretty agile. There it was on a shelf, among a lot of glass containers of alcohol, preserving everything from giant tapeworms to Ghulam Qadir's penis and testicles.'

'Ghulam Qadir?'

'Don't you know your history? He was the fellow who blinded the Emperor Shah Alam. They caught up with him near Saharanpur and cut his balls off. Preserved them for posterity. Waste of alcohol, though. Have another drink, laddie. And then for a sausage. Ah! Sweet Mystery of Life!'

After another drink and several 'mystery' sausages, I made my getaway and stumbled homewards up a narrow path along an open ridge. A jackal slunk ahead of me, and a screech-owl screeched, but I got home safely, none the worse for an evening with the descendant of Bonnie Prince Charlie.

WHO'S BEEN SLEEPING IN MY BED?

There was a break in the rains, the clouds parted, and the moon appeared—a full moon, bathing the mountains in a pollen-yellow light. Little Fosterganj, straddling the slopes of the Ganga–Yamuna watershed, basked in the moonlight, each lighted dwelling a firefly in the night.

Only the Fairy Glen palace was unlit, brooding in the darkness. I was returning from an evening show at the Realto in Mussoorie. It had been a long walk, but a lovely one. I stopped outside the palace gate, wondering about its lonely inhabitants and all that might have happened within its walls. I wanted to see them again, but not at night—not with strange birds flapping around and skeletons hidden in the box-beds. Old skeletons, maybe; but what were they doing there?

I reached Hassan's bakery around midnight, and mounted the steps to my room. My door was open. It was never locked, as I had absolutely nothing that anyone would want to take away. The typewriter, which I had hired from a shop in Dehradun, was a heavy machine, designed for office use; no one was going to carry it off.

But someone was in my bed.

Fast asleep. Snoring peacefully. Not Goldilocks. Nor a bear.

I switched on the light, shook the recumbent figure. He started up. It was Sunil. After giving him a beating, the police had let him go.

'Uncle, you frightened me!' he exclaimed.

He called me 'Uncle', although I was only some fifteen or sixteen years older than him. Call a tiger 'Uncle', and he won't harm you; or so the forest-dwellers say. Not quite how it works out with people approaching middle age. Being addressed as 'Uncle' didn't make me very fond of Sunil.

'I'm the one who should be frightened,' I said. 'A pickpocket in my bed!'

'I don't pick pockets any more, Uncle. I've turned a new leaf. Don't you know that expression?' Sunil had studied up to Class 8 in a 'convent school'.

'Well, you can turn out of my bed,' I said. 'And return that watch you took off me before you got into trouble.'

'You lent me the watch, Uncle. Don't you remember? Here!' He held out his arm. 'Take it back.' There were two watches on his wrist; my modest HMT, and something far more expensive. I removed the HMT and returned it to my own wrist.

'Now can I have my bed back?' I asked.

'There's room for both of us.'

'No, there isn't, it's only a khatiya. It will collapse under our combined weight. But there's this nice easy chair here, and in the morning, when I get up, you can have the bed.'

Reluctantly, Sunil got off the bed and moved over to the cane chair. Perhaps I'd made a mistake. It meant that Sunil would be awake all night, and that he'd want to talk. Nothing can be more irritating than a room companion who talks all night.

I switched off the light and stretched out on the cot. It was a bit wobbly. Perhaps the floor would have been better. Sunil sat in the chair, whistling and singing film songs—something about a red dupatta blowing in the wind, and telephone calls from Rangoon to Dehradun. A romantic soul, Sunil, when he wasn't picking pockets. Did I say there's nothing worse than a companion who talks all night? I was wrong. Even worse is a companion who sings all night.

'You can sing in the morning,' I said. 'When the sun

comes out. Now go to sleep.'

There was silence for about two minutes. Then: 'Uncle?'

'What is it?'

'I have to turn over a new leaf.'

'In the morning, Sunil,' I turned over and tried to sleep.

'Uncle, I have a project.'

'Well, don't involve me in it.'

'It's all seedha-saadha, and very interesting. You know that old man who sells saande-ka-tel—the oil that doubles your manhood?'

'I haven't tried it. It's an oil taken from a lizard, isn't it?'

'A big lizard.'

'So?'

'Well, he's old now and can't go hunting for these lizards. You can only find them in certain places.'

'Maybe he should retire and do something else, then. Grow marigolds. Their oil is also said to be good for lovers.'

'Not as good as lizard oil.'

'So what's your project?' He was succeeding in keeping me awake. 'Are you going to gather lizards for him?'

'Exactly, Uncle. Why don't you join me?'

∽

Next morning Sunil elaborated on his scheme. I was

to finance the tour. We would trek, or use a bus where there were roads, and visit the wooded heights and rocky slopes above the Bhagirathi river, on its descent from the Gangotri glacier. We would stay in rest houses, dharamsalas, or small hotels. We would locate those areas where the monitors, or large rock lizards, were plentiful, catch as many as possible and bring them back alive to Fosterganj, where our gracious mentor would reward us to the tune of two hundred rupees per reptile. Sunil and I would share this bonanza.

The project, if any, did not interest me. I was extremely skeptical of the entire scheme. But I was bored, and it sounded like it could be fun, even an adventure of sorts, and I would have Sunil as guide, philosopher, and friend. He could be a lovely and happy-go-lucky companion—provided he kept his hands out of other people's pockets and did not sing at night.

Hassan was equally skeptical about the success of the project. For one thing, he did not believe in the magical properties of saande-ka-tel (never having felt the need for it); and for another, he did not think those lizards would be caught so easily. But he thought it would be a good thing for Sunil, something different from what he was used to doing. The young man might benefit from my 'intellectual' company. And in the hills, not many folks had money in their pockets.

And so, with the blessings of Hassan, and a modest overdraft from Vishaal, our friendly bank manager, I packed a haversack with essentials (including my favourite ginger biscuits as prepared by Hassan) and set out with Sunil on the old pilgrim road to Tehri and beyond.

Sunil had brought along two large baskets, as receptacles for the lizards when captured. But as he had no intention of carrying them himself—and wisely refrained from asking me to do so—he had brought along a twelve-year-old youth from the bazaar—a squint-eyed, harelipped, one-eared character called Buddhoo, whose intelligence and confidence made up for his looks. Buddhoo was to act as our porter and general factotum. On our outward journey he had only to carry the two empty baskets; Sunil hadn't told him what their eventual contents might be.

It was late July, still monsoon time, when we set out on the Tehri road.

In those days it was still a mule track, meandering over several spurs and ridges, before descending to the big river. It was about forty miles to Tehri. From there we could get a bus, at least up to Pratap Nagar, the old summer capital of the hill state.

ON THE TRAIL OF THE LIZARD

That first day on the road was rather trying. I had done a certain amount of walking in the hills, and I was reasonably fit. Sunil, for all his youth, had never walked further than Mussoorie's cinemas or Dehra's railway station, where the pickings for his agile fingers had always been good. Buddhoo, on the other hand, belied his short stature by being so swift of foot that he was constantly leaving us far behind. Every time we rounded a corner, expecting to find him waiting for us, he would be about a hundred yards ahead, never tiring, never resting.

To keep myself going I would sing either Harry Lauder's 'Keep right on to the end of the road,' or Nelson Eddy's 'Tramp, tramp, tramp'.

> *Tramp, tramp, tramp, along the highway,*
> *Tramp, tramp, tramp, the road is free!*
> *Blazing trails along the byways....*

Sunil did not appreciate my singing.

'You don't sing well,' he said. 'Even those mules are getting nervous.' He gestured at a mule-train that was passing us on the narrow path. A couple of mules were trying to break away from the formation.

'Nothing to do with my singing,' I said. 'All they want are those young bamboo shoots coming up on the hillside.'

Sunil asked one of the mule drivers if he could take a ride on a mule; anything to avoid trudging along the stony path. The mule driver agreeing, Sunil managed to mount one of the beasts, and went cantering down the road, leaving us far behind.

Buddhoo waited for me to catch up. He pointed at a large rock to the side of road, and sure enough, there, resting at ease, basking in the morning sunshine, was an ungainly monitor lizard about the length of my forearm.

'Too small,' said Buddhoo, who seemed to know something about lizards. 'Bigger ones higher up.'

The lizard did not move. It stared at us with a beady eye; a contemptuous sort of stare, almost as if it did not think very highly of humans. I wasn't going to touch it. Its leathery skin looked uninviting; its feet and tail reminded me of a dinosaur; its head was almost serpent like. Who would want to use its body secretions, I wondered. Certainly not if they had seen the creature. But human beings, men especially, will do almost anything to appease their vanity. Tiger's whiskers or saande-ka-tel—anything to improve their sagging manhood.

We did not attempt to catch the lizard. Sunil was supposed to be the expert. And he was already a mile away, enjoying his mule ride.

An hour later he was sitting on the grassy verge, nursing a sore backside. Riding a mule can take the skin off the backside of an inexperienced rider.

'I'm in pain,' he complained. 'I can't get up.'

'Use saande-ka-tel,' I suggested.

Buddhoo went sauntering up the road, laughing to himself.

'He's mad,' said Sunil.

'That makes three of us, then.'

COMPANIONS OF THE ROAD

By noon we were hungry. Hassan had provided us with buns and biscuits, but these were soon finished, and we were longing for a real meal. Late afternoon we trudged into Dhanolti, a scenic spot with great views of the snow peaks; but we were in no mood for scenery. Who can eat sunsets? A forest rest house was the only habitation, and had food been available we could have spent the night there. But the caretaker was missing. A large black dog frightened us off.

So on we tramped, three small dots on a big mountain, mere specks, beings of no importance. In creating this world, God showed that he was a Great Mathematician; but in creating man, he got his algebra wrong. Puffed up with self-importance, we are in fact the most dispensable of all his creatures.

On a long journey, the best companion is usually the one who talks the least, and in that way Buddhoo was a comforting presence. But I wanted to know him better.

'How did you lose your ear?' I asked.

'Bear tore it off,' he said, without elaborating.

Brevity is the soul of wit, or so they say.

'Must have been painful,' I ventured.

'Bled a lot.'

'I wouldn't care to meet a bear.'

'Lots of them out here. If you meet one, run downhill. They don't like running downhill.'

'I'll try to remember that,' I said, grateful for his

shared wisdom. We trudged on in silence. To the south, the hills were bleak and windswept; to the north, moist and well-forested. The road ran along the crest of the ridge, and the panorama it afforded, with the mountains striding away in one direction and the valleys with their gleaming rivers snaking their way towards the plains, gave me an immense feeling of freedom. I doubt if Sunil felt the same way. He was preoccupied with tired legs and a sore backside. And for Buddhoo it was a familiar scene.

A brief twilight, and then, suddenly, it grew very dark. No moon; the stars just beginning to appear. We rounded a bend, and a light shone from a kerosene lamp swinging outside a small roadside hut.

It was not the pilgrim season, but the owner of the hut was ready to take in the odd traveller. He was a grizzled old man. Over the years the wind had dug trenches in his cheeks and forehead. A pair of spectacles, full of scratches, almost opaque, balanced on a nose long since broken. He'd lived a hard life. A survivor.

'Have you anything to eat?' demanded Sunil.

'I can make you dal-bhaat,' said the shopkeeper. Dal and rice was the staple diet of the hills; it seldom varied.

'Fine,' I said. 'But first some tea.'

The tea was soon ready, hot and strong, the way I liked it.

The meal took some time to prepare, but in the meantime we made ourselves comfortable in a corner of the shop, the owner having said we could spend the night there. It would take us two hours to reach the township of Chamba, he said. Buddhoo concurred. He knew the road.

We had no bedding, but the sleeping area was covered with old sheepskins stitched together, and they looked comfortable enough. Sunil produced a small bottle of rum from his shoulder bag, unscrewed the cap, took a swig, and passed it around. The old man declined. Buddhoo drank a little; so did I. Sunil polished off the rest. His eyes became glassy and unfocused.

'Where did you get it?' I asked.

'Hassan Uncle gave it to me.'

'Hassan doesn't drink—he doesn't keep it, either.'

'Actually, I picked it up in the police station, just before they let me go. Found it in the havildar's coat pocket.'

'Congratulations,' I said. 'He'll be looking forward to seeing you again.'

The dal-bhaat was simple but substantial.

'Could do with some pickle,' grumbled Sunil, and then fell asleep before he could complain any further.

᮱

We were all asleep before long. The sheepskin rug was reasonably comfortable. But we were unaware that it harboured a life of its own—a miniscule but active population of fleas and bugs—dormant when undisturbed, but springing into activity at the proximity of human flesh and blood.

Within an hour of lying down we were wide awake.

When God, the Great Mathematician, discovered that in making man he had overdone things a bit, he created the bedbug to even things out.

Soon I was scratching. Buddhoo was up and scratching. Sunil came out of his stupor and was soon cursing and scratching. The fleas had got into our clothes, the bugs were feasting on our blood. When the world as we know it comes to an end, these will be the ultimate survivors.

Within a short time we were stomping around like Kathakali dancers. There was no relief from the exquisite torture of being seized upon by hundreds of tiny insects thirsting for blood or body fluids.

The tea shop owner was highly amused. He had never seen such a performance—three men cavorting around the room, scratching, yelling, hopping around.

And then it began to rain. We heard the first heavy raindrops pattering a rhythm on the tin roof. They increased in volume, beating against the only window and bouncing off the banana fronds in the little courtyard. We needed no urging. Stripping off our clothes, we dashed outside, naked in the wind and rain, embracing the elements. What relief! We danced in the rain until it stopped, and then, getting back into our clothes with some reluctance, we decided to be on our way, no matter how dark or forbidding the night.

We paid for our meal—or rather, I paid for it, being the only one in funds—and bid goodnight and goodbye to our host. Actually, it was morning, about 2 a.m., but we had no intention of bedding down again; not on those sheepskin rugs.

A half-moon was now riding the sky. The rain had refreshed us. We were no longer hungry. We set out with renewed vigour.

Great lizards, beware!

TAIL OF THE LIZARD

At daybreak we tramped into the little township of Chamba, where Buddhoo proudly pointed out a memorial to soldiers from the area who had fallen fighting in the trenches in France during the First World War. His grandfather had been one of them. Young men from the hills had traditionally gone into the army; it was the only way they could support their families; but times were changing, albeit slowly. The towns now had several hopeful college students. If they did not find jobs they could go into politics.

The motor road from Rishikesh passed through Chamba, and we were able to catch a country bus which deposited us at Pratap Nagar later that day.

Pratap Nagar is not on the map, but it used to exist once upon a time. It may still be there, for all I know. Back in the days of the old Tehri Raj it had been the raja's summer capital. There had even been a British resident and a tiny European population—just a handful of British officials and their families. But after Independence, the raja no longer had any use for the place. The state had been poor and backward, and over the years he had spent more time in Dehradun and Mussoorie.

We were there purely by accident, having got into the wrong bus at Chamba.

The wrong bus or the wrong train can often result in interesting consequences. It's called the charm of the unexpected.

Not that Pratap Nagar was oozing with charm. A dilapidated palace, an abandoned courthouse, a dispensary without a doctor, a school with a scatter of students and no teachers, and a marketplace selling sad-looking cabbages and cucumbers—these were the sights and chief attractions of the town. But I have always been drawn to decadent, decaying, forgotten places—Fosterganj being one of them—and while Sunil and Buddhoo passed the time chatting to some of the locals at the bus stand—which appeared to be the centre of all activity—I wandered off along the narrow, cobbled lanes until I came to a broken wall.

Passing through the break in the wall I found myself in a small cemetery. It contained a few old graves. The inscriptions had worn away from most of the tombstones, and on others the statuary had been damaged. Obviously no one had been buried there for many years.

In one corner I found a grave that was better preserved than the others, by virtue of the fact that the lettering had been cut into an upright stone rather than a flat slab. It read:

Dr Robert Hutchinson
Physician to His Highness
Died July 13, 1933
of Typhus Fever
May his soul rest in peace.

Typhus fever! I had read all about it in an old medical dictionary published half a century ago by *The Statesman* of Calcutta and passed on to me by a fond aunt. Not to be confused with typhoid, typhus fever is rare today but sometimes occurs in overcrowded, unsanitary conditions and is definitely spread by lice, ticks, fleas, mites, and other micro-organisms thriving in filthy conditions—such as old sheepskin rugs which have remained unwashed for years.

I began to scratch at the very thought of it.

I remembered more: 'Attacks of melancholia and mania sometimes complicate the condition, which is often fatal.'

Needless to say, I now found myself overcome by a profound feeling of melancholy. No doubt the mania would follow.

I examined the other graves, and found one more victim of typhus fever. There must have been an epidemic. Fortunately for my peace of mind, the only other decipherable epitaph told of the missionary lady who had fallen victim to an earthquake in 1905. Somehow, an earthquake seemed less sinister than a disease brought on by bloodthirsty bugs.

While I was standing there, ruminating on matters of life and death, my companions turned up, and Sunil exclaimed: 'Well done, Uncle, you've already found one!'

I hadn't found anything, being somewhat short-sighted, but Sunil was pointing across to the far wall, where a great fat lizard sat basking in the sun.

Its tail was as long as my arm. Its legs were spread sideways, like a goalkeeper's. Its head moved from side to side, and suddenly its tongue shot out and seized a passing dragonfly. In seconds the beautiful insect was imprisoned in a pair of strong jaws.

The giant lizard consumed his lunch, then glanced at us standing a few feet away.

'Plenty of fat around that fellow,' observed Sunil. 'Full of that precious oil!'

The lizard let out a croak, as though it had something to say on the matter. But Sunil wasn't listening. He lunged forward and grabbed the lizard by its tail. Miraculously, the tail came away in his hands.

Away went lizard, minus its tail.

Buddhoo was doubled up with laughter. 'The tail's no use,' he said. 'Nothing in the tail!'

Sunil flung the tail away in disgust.

'Never mind,' I said. 'Catch a lizard by its tail—make a wish, it cannot fail!'

'Is that true?' asked Sunil, who had a superstitious streak.

'Nursery rhyme from Brazil,' I said.

The lizard had disappeared, but a white-bearded

patriarch was looking at us from over the wall.

'You need a net,' he said. 'Catching them by hand isn't easy. Too slippery.'

We thanked him for his advice; said we'd go looking for a net.

'Maybe a bedsheet will do,' Sunil said.

The patriarch smiled, stroked his flowing white beard, and asked: 'But what will you do with these lizards? Put them in a zoo?'

'It's their oil we want,' said Sunil, and made a sales pitch for the miraculous properties of saande-ka-tel.

'Oh, that,' said the patriarch, looking amused. 'It will irritate the membranes and cause some inflammation. I know—I'm a nature therapist. All superstition, my friends.

You'll get the same effect, even better, with machine oil. Try sewing-machine oil. At least it's harmless. Leave the poor lizards alone.'

And the barefoot mendicant hitched up his dhoti, gave us a friendly wave, and disappeared in the monsoon mist.

TREMORS IN THE NIGHT

Not to be discouraged, we left the ghost town and continued our journey upriver, as far as the bus would take us. The road ended at Uttarkashi, for the simple reason that the bridge over the Bhagirathi had been washed away in a flash flood. The glaciers had been melting, and that, combined with torrential rain in the upper reaches, had brought torrents of muddy water rushing down the swollen river. Anything that came in its way vanished downstream.

We spent the night in a pilgrim shelter, built on a rocky ledge overlooking the river. All night we could hear the water roaring past below us. After a while, we became used to the unchanging sound; it became like a deep silence, and made our sleep deeper. Sometime before dawn, however, a sudden tremor had us trembling out of our cots.

'Earthquake!' shouted Sunil, making for the doorway and banging into the wall instead.

'Don't panic,' I said, feeling panicky.

'It will pass,' said Buddhoo.

The tremor did pass, but not before everyone in the shelter had rushed outside. There was the sound of rocks falling, and everyone rushed back again. 'Landslide!' someone shouted. Was it safer outside or inside? No one could be sure.

'It will pass,' said Buddhoo again, and went to sleep.

Sunil began singing at the top of his voice: 'Pyar kiya to darna kya—Why be afraid when we have loved'. I doubt Sunil had ever been in love, but it was a rousing song with which to meet death.

'Chup, beta!' admonished an old lady on her last pilgrimage to the abode of the gods. 'Say your prayers instead.'

The room fell silent. Outside, a dog started howling.

Other dogs followed his example. No serenade this, but a mournful anticipation of things to come; for birds and beasts are more sensitive to the earth's tremors and inner convulsions than humans, who are no longer sensitive to nature's warnings.

A couple of jackals joined the chorus. Then a bird, probably a nightjar, set up a monotonous croak. I looked at my watch. It was 4 a.m., a little too early for birds to be greeting the break of day. But suddenly there was a twittering and cawing and chattering as all the birds in the vicinity passed on the message that something was amiss.

There was a rush of air and a window banged open.

The mountain shuddered. The building shook, rocked to and fro.

People began screaming and making for the door.

The door was flung open, but only a few escaped into the darkness.

Across the length of the room a chasm opened up. The lady saying her prayers fell into it. So did one or two others. Then the room and the people in it—those who were on the other side of the chasm—suddenly vanished.

There was the roar of falling masonry as half the building slid down the side of the mountain.

We were left dangling in space.

'Let's get out of here quickly!' shouted Sunil.

We scrambled out of the door. In front of us, an empty void. I couldn't see a thing. Then Buddhoo took me by the hand and led me away from the crumbling building and on to the rocky ledge above the river.

The earth had stopped quaking, but the mountain had been shaken to its foundations, and rocks and trees were tumbling into the swollen river. The town was in darkness, the power station having shut down after the first tremor. Here and there a torch or lantern shone out of the darkness, and people could be heard wailing and shouting to each other as they roamed the streets in the rain. Somewhere a siren went off. It only seemed to add to the panic.

At 5 a.m., the rain stopped and the sky lightened. At six it was daybreak. A little later the sun came up. A beautiful morning, except for the devastation below.

THE MOUNTAINS ARE MOVING

'I think I'll join the army,' announced Sunil three days later, when we were back in Fosterganj. 'Do you think they'll take me?'

Sunil had been impressed by the rescue work carried out by the army after the Uttarkashi earthquake.

'Like a flash,' I said. 'Provided you keep your fingers out of the brigadier's pockets.'

∽

In those early hours of the morning, confusion had prevailed in and around Uttarkashi. Houses had crumbled from the tremors and aftershocks, or been buried under the earth and rocks of a number of landslides. Survivors were wandering around in a daze. Many lay crushed or trapped under debris. It would take days, weeks for the town to recover.

At first there were disorganized attempts at rescue, and Sunil, Buddhoo, and I made clumsy attempts to extricate people from the ruins of their homes. A township built between two steep mountains, and teetering along the banks of a moody river, was always going to be at risk. It had happened before, it would happen again.

A little girl, dusty but unhurt, ran to me and asked, 'Will there be school today?'

'I don't think so,' I said.

A small boy was looking for his mother; a mother was searching for her children; several men were digging in the rubble, trying to extricate friends or family members.

And then a couple of army trucks arrived, and the rescue work moved more swiftly, took on a certain momentum. The jawans made all the difference. Many were rescued who would otherwise have perished.

But the town presented a sad spectacle. A busy marketplace had vanished; a school building lay in ruins; a temple had been swallowed up by a gaping wound in the earth.

On the road we met the bearded patriarch, the one we had encountered two days earlier.

'Did you find your lizards?' he asked.

But we had forgotten about lizards.

'What we need now are kitchen utensils,' he said.

'Then we can prepare some food for those who need it.'

He was, it appeared, the head of a social service organization, and we followed him to his centre, a shed near the bus stand, and tried to make ourselves useful. A doctor and nurse were at work on the injured.

I have no idea how many perished, or were badly injured in that earthquake, I was never any good at statistics. Old residents told me that the area was prone to such upheavals.

'Men come and go,' I said, 'but the mountains remain.'

'Not so,' said an old-timer. 'Out here, the mountains are still on the move.'

∽

As soon as the buses were running again, Sunil and I returned to Fosterganj. Buddhoo remained behind, having decided to join the patriarch's aid centre. We missed his good-natured company, even his funny hare-teeth smile. He promised to meet us again. But till the time I left Fosterganj, we were still waiting for him to turn up. I wonder what became of him. Some of the moving forces of our lives are meant to touch us briefly and then go their way.

A GHOST VILLAGE

On our way back, the bus broke down, as buses were in the habit of doing in those good old days. It was shake, rattle, and roll for most of the journey, or at least part of the journey, until something gave way. Occasionally a bus went out of control and plunged over a cliff, taking everyone with it; a common enough occurrence on those hill roads.

We were lucky. Our bus simply broke its axle and came to rest against a friendly deodar tree.

So we were walking again.

Sunil said he knew of a shortcut, and as a result we got lost, just the two of us, everyone else having kept to the main road.

We wandered over hill and dale, through a forest of oak and rhododendron, and then through some terraced fields (with nothing in them) and into a small village which appeared to be inhabited entirely by monkeys. An unfriendly lot of the short-tailed rhesus clan, baring their teeth at us, making guttural sounds and more or less telling us to be off.

There were about fifteen houses in the village, and all of them were empty—except for the monkeys and a colony of field rats. Where were all the people?

Going from house to house, we finally found an old couple barricaded inside a small hut on the outskirts of the village. They were happy to see us. They hadn't seen another human for over a month.

Prem Singh and his wife Chandni Devi were the only people still living in the village. The others had gone away—most of them to towns or cities in the plains, in search of employment, or to stay with friends or relatives; for there was nothing to sustain them in the village. The monkeys by day and the wild boars by night had ravaged the fields. Not a leaf, nor an edible root, remained. Prem Singh and his wife were living on their small store of rice and lentils. Even so, the wife made us tea and apologized that there was no milk or sugar.

'We too will leave soon,' she said. 'We will go to our son in Ludhiana. He works in a factory there.'

And that was what the others had done—gone wherever an earning member of the family had settled.

As it was growing dark, and the couple had offered us the occupancy of a spare room, we decided to stay the night.

An eerie silence enveloped the hillside. No dogs barked.

They were no match for the monkeys. But we were comfortable on our charpais.

Just before daybreak Sunil had to go outside to relieve himself. The nearest field would do, he said; they were all empty anyway. I was still asleep, dreaming of romantic encounters in a rose garden, when I was woken by shouts and a banging of the door, and Sunil rushed in barebottomed and out of breath.

'What happened?' I asked, somewhat disoriented by this ridiculous interruption of my love dream.

'A wild pig came after me!' he gasped. 'One of those with tusks. I got up just in time!'

'But it got your pants, it seems,' I said.

When the sun came up, we both ventured into the

field but there was no sign of a wild pig. By now the monkeys were up and about, and I had a feeling that they had made off with Sunil's pants. Prem Singh came to the rescue by giving him an old pair of pyjamas, but they were much too tight and robbed Sunil of his usual jaunty ebullience. But he had to make to do with them.

The whole situation had provided Prem Singh and his wife with much needed comic relief. In their hopeless predicament they could still find something to laugh at. Sunil invited them to visit his village, and we parted on friendly terms.

And so we limped back to Fosterganj without any lizards, and Sunil without pants; but we had learnt something during the week's events. Life in the hills and remote regions of the country was very different from life in the large towns and cities. And already the drift towards the cities had begun. Would the empty spaces be taken over again by the apes, reptiles, and wild creatures? It was too early to tell, but the signs were there.

Meanwhile, Sunil was still intent on joining the army, and no sooner were we back in Fosterganj than he was off to the recruiting centre in Lansdowne. Would they take him, I wondered. He wasn't exactly army material. But then, neither was Beetle Bailey.

SOME PEOPLE DON'T AGE

As usual, nothing was happening in Fosterganj. Even the earthquake had barely touched it. True, part of Foster's old cottage had collapsed, but it was going to do that anyway. He simply moved into the remaining rooms without bothering about the damaged portion. In any case, there was no money for repairs.

Passing that way a couple of times, I heard the strains of Sir Harry Lauder again. At least the gramophone was still intact!

Hassan had a Murphy radio and had heard about the Uttarkashi earthquake and its aftermath, so he was relieved to see that I was back.

There was a rumour going around that Fairy Glen had been sold, and that it was going to be pulled down to make way for a grand hotel. I wondered what would happen to its occupants, the young-old boy and his equally intriguing mother. And would skeletons be turning up all over the place, now that it was to be dismantled? Or had I imagined that skeletal hand in the box-bed? In retrospect, it seemed more and more like a nightmare.

I dropped in at the bank and asked Vishaal if the rumours were true.

'There's something going on,' he admitted. 'Nothing certain as yet, because there's more than one owner—a claimant in Nepal, another in Calcutta, and a third in Mauritius! But if they come to some agreement there's a hotel group that's interested.'

'Who would want to come to Fosterganj?' I mused.

'Oh, you never know. They say the water here has healing properties.'

'Well, I certainly get diarrhoea pretty frequently.'

'That's because it's pumped up from the dhobi ghat. Don't drink the tap water. Drink the water from upstream.'

'I walked upstream,' I said, 'and I arrived at the burning ghat.'

'Oh, that. But it isn't used much,' said Vishaal. 'Only one or two deaths a year in Fosterganj.'

'They can put that in the brochure, when they build that hotel. But tell me—what will happen to those people living in the palace? They're caretakers, aren't they?

'The boy and his mother? Poor relatives. They'll be given some money. They'll go away.'

I thought it would be charitable on my part to warn the boy and his mother of the impending sale—if they did not know about it already. Quixotic rather than charitable. Or perhaps I just needed an excuse to see them again.

But unwilling to meet skeleton or big black bird, I went there during the day.

It was early September, and the monsoon was beginning to recede. While the foliage on the hillside was still quite lush, autumn hues were beginning to appear. The Virginia creepers, suspended from the oak trees, were turning red. Wild dahlias reared their heads from overhanging rocky outcrops. In the bank manager's garden, chrysanthemums flounced around like haughty maharanis. In the grounds of Fairy Glen, the cosmos had spread all over the place and was just beginning to flower. In the late monsoon light, the old palace looked almost beautiful in its decadence; a pity it would have to go. We need these reminders of history, even though they be haunted, or too grand for their own good.

The boy was out somewhere, but the mother—if, indeed, she was his mother—was at the back of the building, putting out clothes to dry. She smiled when she saw me. The smile spread slowly across her face, like the sun chasing away a shadow, but it also lit up the scar on her cheek.

She asked me to sit down, offered me tea. I declined the tea but sat down on the steps, a bench, and a couple of old chairs being festooned with garments.

'At last I can dry some clothes. After so many days the sun has finally come out.'

Although the boy usually spoke in English, she was obviously more at home in Hindi. She spoke it with a distinct Nepali lilt.

'Well, you haven't seen the sun for days,' I said, 'and I haven't seen the dhobi for weeks. I'm down to my last shirt.'

She laughed. 'You should get married.'

It was my turn to laugh. 'You mean marry a washerwoman? Wives don't wash clothes anymore.'

'But mothers do.' And then she surprised me by adding, 'Wives can also be mothers.'

'There are washing machines now, in England and America,' I said. 'They'll be here soon enough. Expensive, of course. But new things are always expensive. We'll also have television soon.'

'What's that?'

'Radio with pictures. It's in Delhi already. A bit boring but it might catch on. Then you won't have to go to the cinema.'

'I don't go to the cinema. Not since my husband died. He took me once—six or seven years ago. I forget the name of the film, but an actress called Madhubala was in it. She was very pretty.'

'Just like you,' I said.

She looked away. 'I'm not young.'

'Some people don't age. Your son—some say that he's much older than he looks.'

She did not reply, and just then the boy himself appeared, whistling cheerfully and bowing to me as he approached.

'It is good to see you again,' he said. 'The last time you were here, you left in a hurry.'

'I'm sorry, but that was a very creepy room you put me in. There was something in the box-bed. My imagination, probably.'

'A skeleton, probably. Grandfather stored them all over the palace. He didn't like burial grounds or cremations. And in the old days, if you were rich and powerful you could do as you liked.'

'It's the same today,' I said. 'Although not so openly. But I heard the property is being sold, to be pulled down—a hotel will come up. Did you know?'

'If it's true—' a shadow crossed his face, and for a few seconds he looked much older. 'If it's true, then...'

He did not complete what he wanted to say.

'If it happens,' said his mother, 'then we will have to leave. To Nepal, perhaps. Or to Nabha. I have a cousin there. We are Sirmauris on my mother's side.'

'We are not going anywhere,' said the boy, glowering. The brightness had gone from his face. No one likes the thought of being thrown out of a house which has been a home for most of one's life. When I was a boy, my mother and stepfather were constantly being evicted from one house after another. Their fault, no doubt, but I grew up feeling that the world was a hostile place full of rapacious landlords.

'I'll try to find out more,' I said, getting up to leave. 'Vishaal, the bank manager, will know.'

MORNING AT THE BANK

When I called on Vishaal at the bank a day or two later, he was busy with a couple of customers. This was unusual. Busy days in the bank, let alone in Fosterganj, were rare indeed.

The cashier brought in another chair, and I joined the tea party in Vishaal's office. No secrets in Fosterganj. Everyone knew what everyone else had in their accounts, savings or otherwise.

One of the clients was Mr Foster.

He had first presented Vishaal with a basket of eggs, with the proviso that they be distributed among the staff.

'I should have brought sweets,' said Foster, 'but for

sweets I'd have to trudge up to Mussoorie, while the eggs are courtesy my hens. Courtesy your bank, of course.'

'We appreciate them,' said Vishaal. 'We'll have omelettes in the lunch break. So how are the hens doing?'

'Well, a fox got two of them, and a jackal got three, and your guard got my rooster.'

Vishaal looked up at the guard who was standing just outside the door, looking rather stupid.

'Gun went off by mistake,' said the guard.

'It's not supposed to go off at all,' said Vishaal. 'You could kill somebody. It's only for show. If someone holds up the bank, we give them the money. It's all insured.'

The second customer looked interested. A lean, swarthy man in his sixties, he played with the knob of his walnut-wood walking stick and said, 'Talking of insurance, do you know if the Fairy Glen was insured?'

'Don't think so,' said Vishaal. 'It's just a ruin. What is there to insure?'

'It's full of interesting artifacts, I'm told. Old pictures, furniture, antiques.... I'm going there today. The owners have asked me to list anything that may be valuable, worth removing, before they hand over the place to the hotel people.

'So it's really going?' I asked.

'That's right,' he said. 'The deal is all but sealed.'

'And the present occupants?'

'Just caretakers. Poor relatives. I believe the woman was the old raja's keep—or one of them, anyway. They'll have to go.'

'Perhaps the hotel can find some work for them.'

'They want vacant possession.' He got up, twirling his walking stick. 'Well, I must go. Calls to make.'

'You can use our phone,' said Vishaal. 'The only other public phone is at the police outpost, and it's usually out of order. And if you like, I can send for the local taxi.'

'No, I'll call from Mussoorie. I shall enjoy walking back to town. But I might want that taxi later.'

He strode out of the bank, walking purposefully through the late monsoon mist. He was one of the world's middlemen, a successful commission agent, fixing things for busy people. After some time they make themselves indispensable.

Mr Foster was quite the opposite. No one really needed him. But he needed another loan.

'No more chickens,' said Vishaal. 'And you haven't built your poultry shed.'

'Someone stole the wire netting. But never mind the chickens, I've another proposition. Mr Vishaal, sir, what about aromatherapy?'

'What about it? Never heard of such a thing.'

'It's all the rage in France, I hear. You treat different ailments or diseases with different aromas. Calendula for headaches, roses for nervous disorders, gladioli for piles—'

'Gladioli don't have an aroma,' I said.

'Mine do!' exclaimed Foster, full of enthusiasm. 'I can cover the hillside with gladioli. And dahlias too!'

'Dahlias don't have an aroma, either.' I was being Irish again.

'Well then, nasturtiums,' said Foster, not in the least put out. 'Nasturtiums are good for the heart.'

'All right, go ahead,' said Vishaal. 'What's stopping you? You don't need a loan to grow flowers.'

'Ah, but I have to distil the aroma from them.'

'You need a distillery?'

'Something like that.'

'You already have one. That rhododendron wine you made last year wasn't bad. Forget about aromas. Stick to wine and spirits, Mr Foster, and you'll make a fortune. Now I'm off for lunch.'

The bank shut its doors for lunch, and we went our different ways: Vishaal to his rented cottage, Foster to his dilapidated house and poultry farm, and I to Fairy Glen to warn my friends of trouble that lay in store for them.

MORNING AT THE POOL

Over the next two days the assessor, let's call him Mr Middleman, was busy at Fairy Glen, notebook in hand, listing everything that looked as though it might have some value: paintings, furnishings, glassware, chinaware, rugs, carpets, desks, cupboards, antique inkwells, an old grandfather clock (home to a colony of mice, now evicted), and a nude statue of Venus minus an arm. Two or three rooms had been locked for years. These were opened up by Mr Middleman who proceeded to explore them with enthusiasm. Small objects, like silver hand-bowls and cutglass salt cellars, went into his capacious pockets.

The boy and his mother watched all this activity in silence. They had been told to pack and go, but in reality they had very little to pack. The boy had handed over a bunch of keys; he wasn't obliged to do any more.

On the second day, when he had finished his inventory, Mr Middleman said he would be back the next day with a truck and some workmen to help remove all that he had listed—box-beds included. The boy simply shrugged and walked away; his mother set about preparing dinner, the kitchen still her domain. They were in no hurry.

It was almost dark when Mr Middleman set out on his walk back to town. The clouds had parted, and a full moon was coming up over Pari Tibba, Fairy Hill. In the moonlight a big black bird swooped low over the ravished building.

Pockets bulging with mementoes, Mr Middleman strode confidently through the pine forest, his walking stick swinging at his side. A village postman, on his way home, passed him in the gathering darkness. That was the last time Mr Middleman was seen alive.

His body was discovered early next morning by some girls on their way to school. It lay at the edge of the pond, where the boys sometimes came for a swim. But Mr Middleman hadn't been swimming. He was still in his clothes and his pockets were still bulging with the previous day's spoils. He had been struck over the head several times with the clubbed head of his walking stick. Apparently it had been wrenched from his hands by a stronger person, who had then laid into him with a fury of blows to the head. The walking stick lay a few feet away, covered with blood.

AN INSPECTOR CALLS

From then on, events moved quickly.

A jeepful of policemen roamed up and down Fosterganj's only motorable road, looking for potential killers. The bank, the bakery, and the post office were centres of information and speculation.

Fosterganj might have had its mad dogs and professor eating leopards; old skeletons might pop up here and there; but it was a long time since there'd been a proper murder. It was reported in the Dehradun papers (both Hindi and English) and even got mentioned in the news bulletin from All India Radio, Najibabad.

When I walked into Vishaal's small office in the bank, I found him chatting to a police inspector who had come down from Mussoorie to investigate the crime. One of his suspects was Sunil, but Sunil was far away in Lansdowne, making an earnest attempt to enlist in the Garhwal Rifles. And Sunil would have cleaned out the victim's pockets, the only possible motivation being robbery.

The same for Mr Foster, who was also one of the inspector's suspects. He wouldn't have left behind those valuable little antiques. And in any case, he was a feeble old man; he would not have been able to overcome someone as robust as Mr Middleman.

The talk turned to the occupants of Fairy Glen. But the inspector dismissed them as possible suspects: the woman could never have overpowered the assessor; and her son was just a boy.

I could have told him that the boy was much stronger than he looked, but I did not wish to point the finger of suspicion in his direction; or in any direction, for that matter. Mr Middleman was an outsider; his enemies were probably outsiders too.

After the inspector had gone, Vishaal asked: 'So— who do you think did it?'

'I, said the sparrow, with my bow and arrow, I killed Cock Robin!'

'Seriously, though.'

'I, said the fly, with my little eye, I saw him die.' Vishaal raised his hands in exasperation. I decided to be serious. 'We'll know only if there was a witness,' I said. 'Someone who saw him being attacked. But that's unlikely, if it happened after dark. Not many people use that path at night.'

'True. More than one person has fallen into that pond.'

Indeed, before the day was over, the inspector had fallen into the pond. He had been looking for clues at the water's edge, peering down at a tangle of reeds, when he heard an unusually loud flapping of wings. Looking up, he saw a big black bird hovering above him. He had never seen such a bird before. Startled, he had lost his footing and fallen into the water.

A constable dragged him out, spluttering and cursing. Along with the reeds and water weeds that clung to him was a mask made of cloth. It was a small mask, made for a boy.

The inspector threw it away in disgust, along with a drowned rat and a broken cricket bat that had come to the surface with him. Empty a village pond, and you will come up with a lot of local history; but the inspector did not have time for history.

The only person who seemed unperturbed by the murder was Hassan; he had seen people being killed out of feelings of hate or revenge. But here the reasons seemed more obscure.

'Such men make enemies,' he said. 'The go-betweens, the fixers. Someone must have been waiting for him.' He shrugged and went back to his work.

Hassan, a man who loved his work. He loved baking, just as some of us love writing or painting or making things. Most of the children were off to school in the morning, and his wife would be busy washing clothes or cleaning up the mess that children make. The older boys would take turns making deliveries, although sometimes Hassan did the rounds himself. But he was happiest in the bakery, fashioning loaves of bread, buns, biscuits, and other savouries.

The first condition of happiness is that a man must find joy in his work. Unless the work brings joy, the tedium of an aimless life can be soul-destroying.

Something that I had to remember.

A FIRE IN THE NIGHT

It was late evening the same day when I encountered the boy from the palace.

I was strolling through the forest, admiring the mushrooms that had sprung up in damp, shady places. Poisoned, no doubt, but very colourful. Beware of nature's show-offs: the banded krait, the scarlet scorpion, the beautiful belladonna, the ink-squirting octopus. Even so, history shows human beings to be the most dangerous of nature's show-offs. Inimical to each other, given over to greed and insatiable appetites. Nature strikes when roused; man, out of habit and a perverse nature.

The boy still had some of the animal in him, which was what made him appealing.

'I've been looking for you, sir,' he said, as he stepped out of the shadows.

'I did not see you,' I said, startled.

'They've been looking for me. The police. Ever since that fellow was killed.'

'Did you kill him?'

I could see him smile even though it was dark. 'Such a big man? And why bother? They will take the palace anyway.'

He fell into step with me, holding my hand, leading the way; he knew the path and the forest better than I did. They would not find him easily in these hills.

'My mother has a favour to ask of you, sir.'

'Yes?'

'Will you keep something for her?'

'If it's not too big. I can't carry trunks and furniture around. I'm a one-suitcase person.'

'It's not heavy. I have it with me.' He was carrying a small wooden case wrapped in cloth. 'I can't open it here. It contains her jewellery. A number of things. They are all hers, but they will take them from us if they get a chance.'

'They?'

'The owners. The old king's family. Or their friends.'

'So you are going away?'

'We have to. But not before—.' He did not finish what he was going to say. 'You will keep them for us?'

'For how long? I may leave Fosterganj before the end of the year. I will run out of money by then. I'll have to return to Delhi and take up a job.'

'We will get in touch with you. We won't be far.'

'All right, then. Give me the case. I'll have to look inside later.'

'Of course. But don't let anyone else see it. I'll go now. I don't want to be seen.'

He put the wrapped box in my hands, embraced me—it was more of a bear hug, surprising me with its intensity—and made off into the darkness.

I returned to my room with the box, but I did not open it immediately. The door of my room did not fasten properly, and anyone could have walked in. It was only eight o'clock. So I placed the box on a shelf and covered it with my books. No one was going to touch them. Books gather dust in Fosterganj.

Vishaal had asked me over for a drink, and it was past ten when I started walking back to my room again.

Hassan and family were out on the road, along with some other locals. They were speculating on the cause of a bright rosy glow over the next ridge.

'What's happening?' I asked.

'Looks like a fire,' said Hassan. 'Down the Rajpur road.'

'It may be the Fairy Glen palace,' I said.

'Yes, it's in that direction. Let's go and take a look. They might need help.'

Fosterganj did not have a fire engine, and in those days Mussoorie did not have one either, so there was little that anyone could do to put out a major fire.

And this was a major fire.

One section of the palace was already ablaze, and a strong wind was helping the fire to spread rapidly. There was no sign of the boy and his mother. I could only hope that they were safe somewhere, probably on the other side of the building, away from the wind-driven flames.

A small crowd had gathered on the road, and before

long half the residents of Fosterganj were watching the blaze.

'How could it have started?' asked someone.

'Probably an electrical fault. It's such an old building.'

'It didn't have electricity. Bills haven't been paid for years.'

'Then maybe an oil lamp fell over. In this wind anything is possible.'

'Could have been deliberate. For the insurance.'

'It wasn't insured. Nothing to insure.'

'Plenty to insure, the place was full of valuables and antiques. Furniture, mostly. All gone now.'

'What about the occupants—that woman and her boy?'

'Might be gone too, if they were sleeping.'

'Perhaps they did it.'

'But why?'

'They were being forced out, I heard.'

And so the speculation continued, everyone expressing an opinion, and in the meantime the fire had engulfed the entire building, consuming everything within—furniture, paintings, box-beds, skeletons, carpets, curtains, grandfather clock, a century's accumulated finery, all reduced to ashes. Most of the stuff had already outlived its original owner, who had himself been long since reduced to ashes. His heirs had wished to add to their own possessions, but possession is always a fleeting, temporary thing, and now there was nothing.

Towards dawn the fire burnt itself out and the crowd

melted away. Only a shell of the palace remained, with here and there some woodwork still smouldering among the blackened walls. I wandered around the property and the hillside, looking for the boy and his mother, but I did not really expect to find them.

As I set out for home, something screeched in the tallest tree, and the big black bird flew across the road and over the burnt-out palace before disappearing into the forest below.

A HANDFUL OF GEMS

After an early breakfast with Hassan, I returned to my room and threw myself down on my bed. Then I remembered the case that the boy had left with me. I got up to see if it was still where I had hidden it. My books were undisturbed.

So I took the case down from the shelf, placed it on the bed, and prepared to open it. Then I realized I had no key. There was a keyhole just below the lid, and I tried inserting the pointed end of a pair of small scissors, but to no avail; then a piece of wire from the wire netting of the window, but did no better with that. Finally I tried the open end of a safety pin which I had been using on my pyjama jacket; no use. Obviously I was not meant to be a locksmith, or a thief.

Eventually, in sheer frustration, I flung the box across the room. It bounced off the opposite wall, hit the floor, and burst open.

Gemstones and jewellery cascaded across the floor of the room.

When I had recovered from my astonishment and confusion, I made sure the door was shut, then set about collecting the scattered gems.

There were a number of beautiful translucent red rubies, all aglow in the sun that streamed through the open window. I spread them out on my counterpane. I did not know much about gemstones, but they looked genuine enough to me. Presumably they had come from the ruby mines of Burma.

There was a gold bracelet studded with several very pretty bright green emeralds. Where did emeralds come from? South America, mostly. Supposedly my birthstone; but I'd never been able to afford one.

A sapphire, azure, sparkling in a silver neck-chain. A sapphire from Sri Lanka? And a garnet in a ring of gold. I could recognize a garnet because my grandmother had one. When I was small and asked her what it was, she said it was a pomegranate seed.

So there I was, with a small fortune in my hands. Or may be a large fortune. I had never bothered with gemstones before, but I was beginning to get interested. Having them in your hands makes all the difference.

Where should I hide them? Sooner or later someone would disturb my books. I looked around the room; very few places of concealment. But on my desk was a round biscuit tin. One of Hassan's boys used to keep his marbles in it; I had given him more marbles in exchange for the tin, because it made a handy receptacle for my paper-clips, rubber bands, erasers, and such like. These I now emptied into a drawer. The jewels went into the biscuit tin—rubies, emeralds, sapphire, garnet—just like marbles, only prettier.

But I couldn't leave that biscuit tin lying around. One of the boys might come back for it.

On the balcony were several flowerpots; two were empty; one was home to a neglected geranium, another to a moneyplant that didn't seem interested in going anywhere. I put the biscuit tin in an empty pot, and covered it with the geranium, earth, roots and all, and gave it a light watering. It seemed to perk up immediately! Nothing like having a fortune behind you.

I brought the pot into my room, where I could keep an eye on it. The plant would flourish better indoors.

All this activity had sharpened my appetite, and I went down to the bakery and had a second breakfast.

FOSTER MAKES A SALE

In our dear country sensational events come and go, and excitement soon gives way to ennui.

And so it was in Fosterganj. Interest in the murder and the fire died down soon enough, although of course the police and the palace owners continued to make their enquiries.

Vishaal tried to liven up the hillside, spotting another leopard in his back garden. But it was only a dog-lifter, not a man-eater, and since there were very few dogs to be found in Fosterganj after the last rabies scare, the leopard soon moved on.

A milkman brought me a message from Foster one morning, asking me to come and see him.

'Is he ill?' I asked.

'Looks all right,' said the milkman. 'He owes me for two months' supply of milk.'

'He'll give you a laying hen instead,' I said. 'The world's economy should be based on exchange.'

'That's all right,' said the milkman. 'But his hens are dying, one by one. Soon he won't have any left.'

This didn't sound too good, so I made my way over to Foster's and found him sitting in his small patch of garden, contemplating his onions and a few late gladioli.

'No one's buying my gladioli, and my hens are dying,' he said gloomily. An empty rum bottle lay in the grass beside his wobbly cane chair. 'Sorry I can't offer you anything to drink. I've run out of booze.'

'That's all right,' I said. 'I don't drink in the daytime. But why don't you sell onions? They'll fetch a better price than your gladioli.'

'They've all rotted away,' he said. 'Too much rain. And the porcupines take the good ones. But sit down—sit down, I haven't been out for days. Can't leave the hens alone too long, and the gout is killing me.' He removed a slipper and displayed a dirty bare foot swollen at the ankles. 'But tell me—how's the murder investigation going?'

'It doesn't seem to be going anywhere.'

'Probably that boy,' said Foster. 'He's older than he looks. A strange couple, those two.'

'Well, they are missing. Disappeared after the fire.'

'Probably started it. Well, good luck to them. We don't want a flashy hotel in the middle of Fosterganj.'

'Why not? They might buy your eggs—and your gladioli.'

'No, they'd go to town for their supplies.'

'You never know…. By the way, when did Fosterganj last have a murder? Or was this the first?'

'Not the first by any means. We've had a few over the years. Mostly unsolved.'

'The ones in the palace?'

'The disappearing maharanis—or mistresses. Very mysterious. No one really knows what happened to them, except they disappeared. Any remains probably went in that fire. But no one really bothered. The raja's life was his own business, and in those days they did much as they wanted. A law unto themselves.'

A large white butterfly came fluttering up to Foster and sat on his ear. He carried on speaking.

'Then there was that school principal, down near Rajpur. Fanthorne, I think his name was. Suspected his wife of infidelity. Shot her, and then shot himself. Nice and simple. Made it easy for the police and everyone concerned. A good example to all who contemplate murder. Carry out the deed and then turn yourself in or blow your brains out. Why leave a mess behind?'

'Why, indeed. Apart from your brains.'

'Of course you can also hang yourself, if you want to keep it clean. Like poor old Kapoor, who owned the Empire. It went downhill after Independence. No one coming to Mussoorie, no takers for the hotel. He was heavily in debt. He tried setting fire to it for the insurance, but it was such a sturdy old building, built with stones from the riverbed, that it wouldn't burn properly! A few days later old Kapoor was found hanging from a chandelier in the ballroom.'

'Who got the hotel?'

'Nobody. It passed into the Receiver's hand. It's still there, if you want to look at it. Full of squatters and the ghost of old Kapoor. You can see him in the early hours, wandering about with a can of petrol, trying to set fire to the place.'

'Suicide appears to have been popular.'

'Yes, it's that kind of place. Suicidal. I've thought of it once or twice myself.'

'And how would you go about it?'

'Oh, just keep boozing until I pass out permanently.'

'Nice thought. But don't do it today—not while I'm here.'

'I was coming to that—why I asked you to come over. I was wondering if you could lend me a small sum— just to tide me over the weekend. I'm all out of rations and the water supply has been cut too. Have to fill my bucket at the public tap, after all those washerwomen. Very demeaning for a sahib!'

'Well, I'm a little short myself,' I said. 'Not a good time for writers. But I can send you something from the bakery, I have credit there.'

'Don't bother, don't bother. You wouldn't care to buy a couple of hens, would you? I'm down to just three or four birds.'

'Where would I keep them? But I'll ask Hassan to take them off you. He'll give you a fair price.'

'Fine, fine. And there's my furniture. I could part with one or two pieces. That fine old rocking chair—been in the family for a century.'

I had seen the rocking chair on my previous visit, and had refrained from sitting in it, as it had looked rather precarious.

'I would laze in it all day and get no work done,' I said.

'What about Uncle Fred's skull? It's a real museum piece.'

'No, thanks. It's hardly the thing to cheer me up on a lonely winter's evening. Unlike your gramophone, which is very jolly.'

'Gramophone! Would you like the gramophone?' The white butterfly jumped up a little, as excited as Foster, then settled back on his ear.

'Well, it only just occurred to me—but you wouldn't want to part with it.'

'I might, if you made me a good offer. It's a solid HMV 1942 model. Portable, too. You can play it on a beach in Goa or a mountaintop in Sikkim. Springs are in good condition. So's the handle. Four hundred rupees, and you get the records free. It's a bargain!'

How do you bargain with a Scotsman? Foster's urgent need of money overrode his affection for the ballads of Sir Harry Lauder. I offered him two hundred, which was all the money I had on me. After a good deal of haggling we settled on three hundred. I gave him two and promised to pay the rest later.

In good spirits now, Foster suddenly remembered he had some booze stashed away somewhere after all. We celebrated over a bottle of his best hooch, and I stumbled home two hours later, the gramophone under one arm and a box of records under the other.

That night I treated myself to Sir Harry Lauder singing 'Loch Lomond', Dame Clara Buck singing 'Comin' through the Rye', and Arthur Askey singing 'We Have No Bananas Today'. Hassan's children attended the concert, and various passers-by stopped in the road, some to listen, others to ask why I couldn't play something more pleasing to the ear. But everyone seemed to enjoy the diversion.

TREASURE HUNT

The nights were getting chilly, and I needed another blanket. The rains were over, and a rainbow arched across the valley, linking Fosterganj to the Mussoorie ridge. A strong wind came down from Tibet, rattling the rooftops.

I decided to stay another month, then move down to Rajpur.

∽

Someone had slipped a letter under my door. I found it there early one morning. Inside a plain envelope was a slip of paper with a few words on it. All it said was: 'Chakrata. Hotel Peak View. Next Sunday'.

I presumed the note was from the boy or his mother. Next Sunday was just three days away, but I could get to Chakrata in a day. It was a small military cantonment half way between Mussoorie and Simla. I had been there as a boy, but not in recent years; it was still a little off the beaten track.

I did not tell Hassan where I was going, just said I'd be back in a day or two; he wasn't the sort to pry into my affairs. I stuffed a change of clothes into a travel bag, along with the little box containing the jewels. Before hiding it, I had taped the lid town with Sellotape. It was still under the geranium, and I removed it carefully and returned the plant to its receptacle, where it would now have a little more freedom to spread its roots.

I took a bus down to Dehradun, and after hanging around the bus station for a couple of hours, found one that was going to Chakrata. It was half empty. Only a few village folk were going in my direction.

A meandering road took us through field and forest, and then we crossed the Yamuna just where it emerged from its mountain fastness, still pure and unpolluted in its upper reaches. The road grew steeper, more winding, ascending through pine and deodar forest, and finally we alighted at a small bus stop, where an old bus and two or three ponies appeared to be stranded. A deserted church and a few old graves told me that the British had once been present here.

There was only one hotel on the outskirts of the town, and it took me about twenty minutes to get to it, as I had to walk all the way. It stood in a forest glade, but it did provide a view of the peaks, the snow-capped Chor range being the most prominent.

It was a small hotel, little more than a guesthouse, and I did not notice any other residents. There was no sign of a manager, either; but a gardener or handyman led me to the small reception desk and produced a register. I entered my name and my former Delhi address. He then took me to a small room and asked me if I'd like some tea.

'Please,' I said. 'And something to eat.'

'No cook,' he said. 'But I'll bring you something from the market.' And he disappeared, leaving me to settle down in my room.

I needed a wash, and went into the bathroom. It had a nice view, but there was no water in the tap. There was a bucket half filled with water, but it looked rather murky. I postponed the wash.

I settled down in an armchair, and finding it quite comfortable, immediately fell asleep. Being a man with an easy conscience I've never had any difficulty in falling asleep.

I woke up about an hour later, to find the cook-gardener-caretaker hovering over me with a plate of hot pakoras and a pot of tea. He had only one eye, which, strangely, I hadn't noticed before. I recalled the old proverb: 'In the country of the blind the one-eyed man is king.' But I'd always thought the antithetical was true, and a more likely outcome, in the country of the blind, would be the one-eyed man being stoned to death. How dare he be different.

My one-eyed man seemed happy to talk. Not many tourists came to Chakrata; the intelligence department took a strong interest in visitors. In fact, I could expect a visit from them before the day was out.

'Has anyone been asking for me?' I asked. 'A young man accompanied by his mother?'

'They were here last week. Said they were from Nepal. But they left in a hurry. They did not take your name.'

'Perhaps they'll be back. I'll stay tonight—leave in the morning. Will that be all right?'

'Stay as long as you like. It's ten rupees a day for the room and two rupees for a bucket of water. Water shortage.'

'And it's been raining for three months.'

'But we are far from the river,' he said. And then he left me to my own devices.

It was late evening when he appeared again to inform

me that there were people in the hall who wanted to see me. Assuming that the boy and his mother had arrived, I said, 'Oh, show them in,' and got up from the armchair to receive them.

Three men stepped into the room.

They were total strangers.

One of them asked to see my passport.

'I don't have one,' I said. 'Never left the country.'

'Any identification?'

I shook my head. I'd never been asked for identification. This was 1961, and border wars, invasions, insurrections, and terrorist attacks were all in the future. We were free to travel all over the country without any questions being asked.

One of the three was in uniform, a police inspector. The second, the man who had spoken to me, was a civilian but clearly an official. The third person had some personal interest in the proceedings.

'I think you have something to deliver,' he said. 'Some stones belonging to the royal family.'

'You represent the royal family?' I asked.

'That is correct.'

'And the people who looked after the property?'

'They were servants. They have gone missing since the fire. Are you here to meet them?'

'No,' I said. 'I'm a travel writer. I'm writing a book on our hill stations. Chakrata is one of them.'

'But not for tourists,' said the official. 'This is purely a military station now.'

'Well, I have yet to see a soldier. Very well camouflaged.'

'Soldiers are not deployed here. It is a scientific establishment.'

I thought it better to leave it at that. I had come to the place simply to deliver some gemstones, and not as a spy; I said as much.

'Then may we have the stones?' said the third party. 'You will then be free to leave, or to enjoy the hospitality of this hotel.'

'And if I don't hand them over?'

'Then we may have to take you into custody,' said the inspector. 'For being in possession of stolen property.' And without further ado, he picked up my travel bag, placed it on a table, and rummaged through the contents. With three men standing over me, and the gardener in the background, there was no point in trying to be a hero.

The biscuit tin was soon in his hands. He shook it appreciatively, and it responded with a pleasing rattle. He tore off the tape, pressed open the lid and emptied the contents on the table.

Some thirty or forty colourful marbles streamed across the table, some rolling to the ground, others into the hands of the inspector, who held them up to the light and exclaimed, 'But these are not rubies!'

'My marble collection,' I said. 'And just as pretty as rubies.'

THE GREAT TRUCK RIDE

What had happened, quite obviously, was that Hassan's children, or at least one of them, had seen me secrete the box in the geranium pot. Wanting it back, they had unearthed it while I was out, removed the gemstones and replaced them with their store of marbles.

But what on earth had they done with the jewels? Hidden them elsewhere, perhaps. Or more likely, being still innocent children, they had seen the gems as mere rubbish and thrown them out of my window, into the ravine.

If I got back safely, I'd have to search the ravine.

But I was still in Chakrata, and my interlocutors had told me not to leave before morning. They were still hoping that the boy and his mother, or someone on their behalf, might have followed me to Chakrata.

The three gentlemen left me, saying they'd be back in the morning. I was left with the one-eyed gardener.

'When does the first bus leave for Dehradun?' I asked.

'At ten tomorrow.'

'Are there no taxis here?'

'Who would want a taxi? There is nothing to see. The best view is from your window.'

I gave him five rupees and asked him to bring me some food. He came back with some puris and a potato curry, and I shared it with him. He became quite chatty, and told me the town hadn't been off-bounds in the past, but security had been tightened since some border intrusions by the Chinese. Relations with China had soured ever since the Dalai Lama and his followers had fled to India two years previously. The Dalai Lama was still living in Mussoorie. Chakrata was, in a way, a lookout point; from here, the passes to the north could be better monitored. I'd come to the wrong place at the wrong time.

'I'm no spy,' I said. 'I'll come some other time to enjoy the scenery. I'll be off in the morning.'

'If they let you go.'

That sounded ominous.

The gardener-caretaker left me in order to lock up for the night, and I lay down on my bed in my clothes, wondering what I should do next. I was never much good in an emergency, and I was feeling quite helpless. Without friends, the world can seem a hostile place.

After some time I heard the door being bolted from outside. I'd been locked in.

I hate being locked into rooms. Once, as a small boy, I broke an expensive vase, and as punishment my grandmother locked me in the bathroom. I tried kicking the door open, and when that didn't work, I got hold of a water jug, smashed open a window, and climbed out; only to receive further punishment, by way of being sent to bed without any dinner.

And now I did more or less the same thing, but I waited for an hour or two, to give the gardener time to retire for the night. Then I unlatched the window—no need to break any glass—and peered out into the night.

The moon was a melon, just coming up over the next mountain. There was a vegetable patch just below the window. A cluster of cucumbers stood out in the mellow light. As I did not want to be encumbered with things to carry, I abandoned my travel bag and its meager contents; I would survive without pyjamas and a tattered old sweater. I climbed out on the window ledge and dropped into the vegetable patch, avoiding the cucumbers but pitching forward into a clump of nettles.

The nettles stung me viciously on the hands and face, and I cursed in my best Hindustani. The European languages have their strengths, but for the purposes of cursing out loud you can't beat some of the Indian languages for range and originality.

It took about twenty minutes for the pain of the nettle stings to subside, and by then my linguistic abilities were exhausted. But the nettles had given greater urgency to my flight, and I was soon on the motor road, trudging along at a good pace. I was beginning to feel like a character in a John Buchan novel, always on the move and often in the wrong direction. All my life had been a little like that. But I wouldn't have known any other way to live.

I knew I had to go downhill, because that was the way to the river. After walking for an hour, I was hoping someone would come along and give me a lift. But there would be few travellers at that late hour. Jackals bayed, and an owl made enquiring sounds, but that was all....

And then I heard the approach of heavy vehicles—

not one, but several—and a convoy of army trucks came down the road, their headlights penetrating the gloom and leaving no corner of the road in shadow.

I left the road and stood behind a walnut tree until they had passed. I had no intention of taking a lift in an army truck; I could end up at some high-altitude border post, abandoned there in sub-zero temperatures.

So I returned to the road only when the last truck had gone round the bend, then continued to tramp along the highway, sore of foot but strong of heart. Harry Lauder would have approved.

Something else was coming down the road. Another truck. An old one, rattling away and groaning as it changed gear on a sudden incline. The army wouldn't be using an old wreck. So I stood in the middle of the road and waved it to a stop. An elderly Sardarji, older than the truck, looked out of his cabin window and asked me where I was headed.

'Anywhere,' I said. 'Wherever you're going.'

'Herbertpur,' he said. 'Get in the back.'

Herbertpur was a small township near the Timli Pass, on the old route to Dehradun. Herbert had been a tea-planter back in the 1860s or thereabouts. The family had died out, but the name remained.

I would have liked to sit up front, but Sardarji already had a companion, his assistant, about half my age and fair of face, who showed no signs of making way for me. So I made my way to the back of the truck and climbed into its open body, expecting to find it loaded with farm produce. Instead, I found myself landing in the midst of a herd of goats.

There must have been about twenty of them, all crammed into the back of the truck. Before I could get out, the truck started, and I found myself a fellow traveller with a party of goats destined for a butcher's shop in Herbertpur.

I must say they tried to make me welcome. As the truck lurched along the winding road, we were thrown about a good deal, and I found myself in close contact with those friendly but highly odorous creatures.

Why do we eat them, I wonder. There can be nothing tougher than the meat of a muscular mountain goat. We should instead use them as weapons of offence, driving herds of goats into enemy territory, where they will soon consume every bit of greenery—grass, crops, leaves—in a matter of minutes. Sometimes I wonder why the Great Mathematician created the goat; hardly one of nature's balancing factors.

But I was the intruder, I had no right to any of their space. So I could not complain when a kid mistook me for its mother and snuggled up to me, searching for an udder. When I thrust it away, a billy goat got annoyed and started butting me on the rump. Fortunately for me, two female goats came to my rescue, coming between me and the aggressive male.

By the time we reached Herbertpur it was two in the morning, and I was feeling like a serving of rogan josh or mutton keema, two dishes that I resolved to avoid if ever I saw a menu again.

When I scrambled out of that truck, I was smelling to high heaven. The goats were bleating, as though they missed me. I thanked Sardarji for the lift, and he offered to take me further—all the way to Saharanpur. The goats, he said, would soon be unloaded, and replaced by a pair of buffaloes.

I decided to walk.

There was a small canal running by the side of the road.

There was just one thing I wanted in life. A bath.

I jumped into the canal, clothes and all, and wallowed there until daylight.

RUBIES IN THE DUST

I was back in Fosterganj that same evening, but I waited near the pool until it was dark before returning to my room. My clothes were in a mess, and I must have looked like the Creature from the Black Lagoon or an explorer who had lost his way in the jungle. After another bath, this time with good old Lifebuoy soap, I changed into my last pair of pyjamas, and slept all through the night and most of the next day, only emerging from my room because hunger had overcome lassitude. Hassan fed me on buns, biscuits, and boiled eggs while I gave him an edited account of my excursion. He did not ask any questions, simply told me to avoid areas which were in any way under surveillance. Sage advice.

Over the next week, nothing much happened, except that the days grew shorter and the nights longer and I needed a razai at night.

I inspected all the flowerpots, emptying them one by one, just in case the marble players had switched the hiding place of the gemstones. The children watched me with some amusement, and I had to pretend that I was simply repotting the geraniums and begonias. It was the season for begonias; they flamed scarlet and red and bright orange, challenging the autumn hues of dahlias and chrysanthemums. Early October was a good time for flowers in Fosterganj. Vishaal's wife had created a patch of garden in front of the bank; the post office veranda had been brightened up; and even Foster's broken-down cottage was surrounded by cosmos gone wild.

I searched the ravine below the bakery, in case the gems had been thrown down from my window. I found broken bottles, cricket balls, old slippers, chicken bones, the detritus that accumulates on the fringes of human habitations; but nothing resembling jewellery.

And then one morning, as I was returning from a walk in the woods, I encountered the poor woman who was sweeping the road. This chore was usually carried out by her husband, but he had been ill for some time and she had taken over his duties. She was a sturdy woman, plain-looking and dressed in a faded sari. Even when sweeping the road she had a certain dignity—an effortless, no-fuss dignity that few of us possess.

When I approached, she was holding something up to the light. And when she saw me, she held it out on her palm, and asked, 'What is this stone, Babuji? It was lying here in the dust. It is very pretty, is it not?'

I looked closely at the stone. It was not a pebble, but a ruby, of that I was certain.

'Is it valuable?' she asked. 'Can I keep it?'

'It may be worth something,' I said. 'But don't show it to everyone. Just keep it carefully. You found it, you keep it.'

'Finder's keepers', the philosophy of my school days. And whom did it belong to, anyway? Who were the rightful owners of those stones? There was no way of telling.

And what was their real worth? We put an artificial value on pretty pebbles found in remote places. Just bits of crystals, poor substitutes for marbles. Innocent children know their true worth. Nothing more than the dust at their feet.

The good lady tied the stone in a corner of her sari and lumbered off, happy with her find. And I hoped she'd find more. Better in her hands than in the hands of princes.

SUNIL IS BACK

Out of the blue, Sunil arrived. There he was, lean and languid, sitting on the bakery steps, waiting for me to return from my walk.

'I thought you'd joined the army,' I said.

'They wouldn't take me. I couldn't pass the physical. You have to be an acrobat to do some of those things, like climbing ropes or swinging from trees like Tarzan.'

'All out of date,' I said. 'They need less brawn and more brain.'

He followed me up the steps to my room and stretched himself out on the cot. He reminded me of a cat, sleek and utterly self-satisfied.

'So what else happened?' I asked.

'Well, the colonel was a nice chap. He couldn't enlist me, but he gave me a job in the mess room. You know, keeping the place tidy, polishing the silver, helping at the bar. It wasn't hard work, and sometimes I was able to give myself a rum or a vodka on the quiet. Lots of silver trophies on the shelves. Very tempting, but you can't do much with those things, they are mostly for show.'

'What made you leave?'

'Ivory. There were these elephant's tusks mounted on the wall, you see. Huge tusks. They'd been there for years. The elephant had been shot by a colonel-shikari about fifty years ago, and the tusks put on display in the mess. All that ivory! Very tempting.'

'You can't just pocket elephant tusks.'

'Not pocket them, but you can carry them off. And I knew how to get into that mess room in the middle of the night without anyone seeing me.'

'So did you get away with them?'

'Perfectly. I had a rug in which I hid the tusks, and

I'd tied them up with a couple of good army belts. I took the bus down to Kotdwar without any problem. No one was going to miss those tusks—not for a day or two, anyway.'

'So what went wrong?'

'Things went wrong at the Kotdwar railway station. I was walking along the platform with the rug on my shoulder, looking for an empty compartment, when a luggage trolley bumped into me. I dropped the rug and it burst open. The tusks were there for all to see. A couple of railway police were coming down the platform, so I took off like lightning. Ran down the platform until it ended, then crossed the railway lines and hid in a sugarcane field. Later, I took a ride on a bullock-cart until I was well away from the town. Then I borrowed a bicycle and rode all the way to Najibabad.'

'Where's the cycle?'

'Left it outside the police station just in case the owner came looking for it.'

'Very thoughtful of you. So here you are.'

He smiled at me. He was a rogue. But at least he'd stopped calling me uncle.

ॐ

It was only later that day—towards evening, in fact—that Sunil spotted the gramophone in a corner of my room.

'What's this you've got?' he asked.

'Mr Foster's gramophone. It plays music.'

'I know that. My grandfather has one. He plays old Saigal records.'

'Well, this one has old English records. You won't care for them. I bought the gramophone and the records came with it.'

Sunil lost no time in placing the gramophone on the table, opening it, and putting a record on the turntable. But the table was stuck.

'It's fully wound,' said Sunil. 'There's something jammed inside.'

'It was all right when I went away. The kids must have been fooling around with it.'

'Have you a screwdriver?'

'No, but Hassan will have one. I'll go and borrow it.'

I left Sunil fiddling about with the gramophone, and went downstairs, and came back five minutes later with a small screwdriver. Sunil took it and began unscrewing the upper portion of the gramophone. He opened it up; revealing the springs, inner machinery, the emerald bracelet, garnet broach, and sapphire ring.

Sunil immediately slipped the ring on to a finger and said, 'Very beautiful. Did it come with the gramophone?'

SAPPHIRES ARE UNLUCKY

'Sapphires are unlucky,' I told him. 'You have to be very special to wear a sapphire.'

'I'm lucky,' he said, holding his hands to the light

and admiring the azure stone in its finely crafted ring. 'It suits me, don't you think? And where did all this treasure come from?'

There was no point in making up a story. I told him how the jewels had come into my possession. Even as I did, I wondered who had put the jewellery in the gramophone. One of the children, I presumed—only a child would recognize the value of jewels but not of gemstones. I thought it best not to tell Sunil this. I did not mention the rubies, either. I did not want him hunting all over Fosterganj for them, and interrupting games of marbles to check if the children were playing with rubies.

'Those two won't be back,' he said, referring to the palace boy and his mother. 'They will be wanted for theft, arson, and murder. But others may be after these pretty pebbles.'

'I know,' I said, and told him about my visitors in Chakrata.

'And you will get visitors here as well. I think we should go away for some time. Come to my village. Not the one near Rajpur. I mean my mother's village in Bijnor, on the other side of the Ganga. It's an out-of-the-way place, far from the main highways. Strangers won't be welcome.'

'Will I be welcome?'

'With me, you will always be welcome.'

I allowed Sunil to take over. I wasn't really interested in the stones, they were more trouble than they were worth. All I wanted was a quiet life, a writing pad, books to read, flowers to gaze upon, and sometimes a little love, a little kiss.... But Sunil was fascinated with the gems. Like a magpie, he was attracted to all that glittered.

He transferred the jewels to a small tin suitcase, the kind that barbers and masseurs used to carry around. It was seldom out of his sight. He told me to pack a few things, but to leave my books and the gramophone behind; we did not want any heavy stuff with us.

'You can't carry a palace around,' he said. 'But you can carry the king's jewels.'

'Take that sapphire off,' I said. 'Unless it's your birthstone, it will prove to be unlucky.'

'Well, I don't know my date of birth. So I can wear anything I like.'

'It doesn't suit you. It makes you look too prosperous.'

'Seeing it, people won't suspect that I'm after their pockets.'

He had a point there. And he wasn't going to change his ways.

You have to accept people as they are, if you want to live with them. You can't really change people. Only a chameleon can change colour, and then only in order to deceive you.

If, like Sunil, you have a tendency to pick pockets, that tendency will always be there, even if one day you become a big corporate boss. If, like Foster, you have spent most of your life living on the edge of financial disaster, you will always be living on the edge. If, like Hassan, you are a singleminded baker of bread and maker of children, you won't stop doing either. If, like Vishaal, you are obsessed with leopards, you won't stop looking for them. And if, like me, you are something of a dreamer, you won't stop dreaming.

GANGA TAKES ALL

'Ganga-maiki jai!'

The boat carrying pilgrims across the sacred river was ready to leave. Sunil and I scrambled down the river bank and tumbled into it. It was already overloaded, but we squeezed in amongst the pilgrims, mostly rural folk who had come to Hardwar to visit the temples and take home bottles of Ganga water—in much the same way that the faithful come to Lourdes, in France, and carry away the healing waters of a sacred stream. People are the same everywhere.

In those days there was no road bridge across the Ganga, and the train took one to Bijnor by a long and circuitous route. Sunil's village was off the beaten track, some thirty miles from the nearest station. The easiest way to get there was to cross the river by boat and then take an ekka, or ponycart, to get to the village.

The boat was meant to take about a dozen people, but for a few rupees more the boatmen would usually take in more than the permitted number. When we set off, there must have been at least twenty in the boat—men, women, and children.

'*Ganga-maiki jai!*' they chanted, as the two oarsmen swung into the current.

For a time, all went well. In spite of its load, the boat made headway, being carried a little downstream but in the general direction of its landing place. Then halfway across the river, where the water was deep and strong, the boat began to wobble about and water slopped in over the sides.

The singing stopped, and a few called out in dismay. There was little one could do, except urge the oarsmen on.

They did their best, straining at the oars, the sweat pouring down their bare bodies. We made some progress, although we were now drifting with the current.

'It doesn't matter where we land,' I said, 'as long as we don't take in water.'

I had always been nervous in small boats. The fear of drowning had been with me since childhood: I'd seen a dhow go down off the Kathiawar coast, and bodies washed ashore the next day.

'*Ganga-maiki jai!*' called one or two hardy souls, and we were about two-thirds across the river when water began to fill the boat. The women screamed, the children cried out.

'Don't panic!' I yelled, though filled with panic. 'It's not so deep here, we can get ashore.'

The boat struck a sandbank, tipped over. We were in the water.

I was waist-deep in water, but the current was strong, taking me along. The menfolk picked up the smaller children and struggled to reach the shore. The women struggled to follow them.

Two of the older women were carried downstream; I have no idea what happened to them.

Sunil was splashing about near the capsized boat. 'Where's my suitcase?' he yelled.

I saw it bobbing about on the water, just out of his reach. He made a grab for it, but it was swept away. I saw it disappearing downstream. It might float for a while, then sink to the bottom of the river. No one would find it there. Or some day the suitcase would burst open, its contents carried further downstream, and the emerald bracelet will be washed up among the pebbles of the riverbed. A fisherman might find it. In older times he would have taken it to his king. In present times he would keep it.

We struggled ashore with the others and sank down on the sand, exhausted but happy to be alive.

Those who still had some strength left sang out: '*Ganga-maiki jai!*' And so did I.

Sunil still had the sapphire ring on his hand, but it hadn't done him much good.

END OF THE ROAD

We stayed in Sunil's village for almost a month. I have to say I enjoyed the experience, in spite of the absence of modern conveniences. Electricity had come to the village—which was surprising for that time—and in our room there was a ceiling fan and an old radio. But sanitation was basic, and early in the morning one had to visit a thicket of thorn bushes, which provided more privacy than the toilets at the bus stop. Water came from an old well. It was good sweet water. There were pigeons nesting in the walls of the well, and whenever we drew up a bucket of water the pigeons would erupt into the air, circle above us, and then settle down again.

There were other birds. Parrots, green and gold, settled in the guava trees and proceeded to decimate the young fruit. The children would chase them away, but they would return after an hour or two.

Herons looked for fish among the hyacinths clogging up the village pond. Kingfishers swooped low over the water. A pair of Sarus cranes, inseparable, treaded gingerly through the reeds. All on fishing expeditions.

The outskirts of an Indian village are a great place for birds. You will see twenty to thirty species in the course of a day. Blue jays doing their acrobatics, sky-diving high above the open fields; cheeky bulbuls in the courtyard; seven sisters everywhere; mynahs quarrelling on the veranda steps; scarlet minivets and rosy pastors in the banyan tree; and at night, the hawk cuckoo or brain fever bird shouting at us from the mango-tope.

Almost every village has its mango-tope, its banyan tree, its small temple, its irrigation canal. Old men smoking hookahs; the able-bodied in the fields; children playing gulli-danda or cricket. An idyllic setting, but I did not envy my hosts. They toiled from morn till night—ploughing, sowing, reaping, always with an eye on the clouds—and then having to sell, in order to buy....

Sunil's uncle urged him to stay, to help them on the farm; but he was too lazy for any work that required physical exertion. Towns and cities were his milieu. He was fidgety all the time we were in the village. And when I told him it was time for me to start working, looking for a job in Delhi, he did not object to my leaving but instead insisted on joining me. He too would find a job in Delhi, he said. He could work in a hotel or a shop or even start his own business.

And so I found myself back in my old room in dusty Shahdara in Delhi, and within a short time I'd found work with a Daryaganj publisher, polishing up the English of professors who were writing guides to Shakespeare, Chaucer, and Thomas Hardy.

Sunil had friends in Delhi, and he disappeared for long periods, turning up only occasionally, when he was out of pocket or in need of somewhere to spend the night.

And then one of his friends came by to tell me he'd been arrested at the New Delhi railway station. He'd been back to his old ways, relieving careless travellers of their cash or wristwatches. He was a skilful practitioner of his art, but he'd grown careless.

The police took away the sapphire ring, and of course he never saw it again. It must have brought a little affluence but not much joy to whoever flaunted it next.

Denied bail, Sunil finally found himself lodged in a new, modern jail that had come up at a village called Tihar, on the old Najafgarh road. As a boy I'd gone fishing in the extensive Najafgarh Jheel, but now much of it had been filled in and built over. The herons and kingfishers had moved on, the convicts had moved in.

Sunil had been there a few months when at last I was able to see him. He was looking quite cheerful, not in the least depressed; but then, he was never the despondent type. He was working in the pharmacy, helping out the prison doctor. He had become popular with the inmates, largely due to his lively renderings of Hindi film songs.

Our paths had crossed briefly, and now diverged. I knew we would probably not see each other again. And we didn't. What became of him? Perhaps he spent many more months in jail, making up prescriptions for ailing dacoits, murderers, embezzlers, fraudsters, and sexual offenders; and perhaps when he came out, he was able to start a chemist's shop. Unlikely, but possible. In any case, he would have made Delhi his home. The big city would have suited him.

Fosterganj was a far cry from all this, and I was too busy to give it much thought. And then one Sunday, when I was at home, I had a visitor.

It was Hassan.

He had come to Delhi to attend a relative's marriage and he had got my address from the publisher in Daryaganj. Having given up any hope of seeing me again in Fosterganj, he'd brought along my books, typewriter, and the gramophone.

He spent all morning with me, bringing me up to date on happenings in Fosterganj.

Vishaal had been transferred, getting a promotion, and taking over a branch in the heart of Madhya Pradesh. Mowgli country! Leopard country! Vishaal would be happy there.

'And how's old Foster?' I asked.

'Not too good. He says he won't last long, and he may be right. He wants to know if you'll accept his uncle's skull as a gift.'

'Tell him to gift it to the Mussoorie municipality. I believe they are starting a museum in the Clock Tower. But thanks for bringing the gramophone down. I could do with a little music.'

Hassan then told me that the hotel was now coming up on the site of the old palace. It would be a posh sort of place, very expensive.

'What are they calling it?' I asked.

'Lake View Hotel.'

'But there isn't a lake.'

'They plan to make one. Extend the old pool, and feed it with water from the dhobi ghat. Fosterganj is changing fast.'

'Well, as long as it's good for business. Should be good for the bakery.'

'Oh, they'll have their own bakery. But I'll manage. So many workers and labourers around now. Population is going up. So when will you visit us again?'

'Next year, perhaps. But I can't afford Lake View Palaces.'

'You don't need to. Your room is still there.'

'Then I'll come.'

ᴄ

Over the next three or four years I lost touch with Fosterganj. My life changed a little. I found companionship when I was least expecting it, and I became a freelance writer for a travel magazine. It was funded by a Parsi gentleman who was rumoured to own half of Bombay. I saw no evidence of the wealth in the cheques I received for my stories, but at least I got to travel a lot, zipping around the country by train, bus and, on one occasion, a dilapidated old Dakota of the Indian Airlines.

The forests of Coonoor; the surge of the sea at Gopalpur; old settlements on the Hooghly; the ghats of Banaras; the butterflies of the Western Ghats; the forts of Gwalior; the sacred birds of Mathura; the gardens of Kashmir—all were grist to my mill, or rather to the portable typewriter which had taken the place of the clumsy old office machine. How could Fosterganj's modest charms compare with the splendours that were on offer elsewhere in the land?

So Fosterganj was far from my thoughts—until one day I picked up a newspaper and came across a news item that caught my attention.

On the outskirts of the hill station of Nahan a crime had been committed. An elderly couple living alone in a sprawling bungalow had been strangled to death. The police had been clueless for several weeks, and the case was almost forgotten, until a lady turned up with information about the killer.

She led them to a spot among the pines behind the bungalow, where a boy was digging up what looked like a small wooden chest. It contained a collection of valuable gemstones. The murdered man had been a well-known jeweller with an establishment in Simla.

The accused claimed that he was a minor, barely fifteen.

And certainly he had looked no older to the police. But the woman told them he was only a few years younger than her, and that she was nearly fifty. She confessed to being his accomplice in similar crimes in the past; it was always gems and jewellery he was after. He had been her lover, she said. She had been under his domination for too long.

I looked at the photograph of the man-boy that accompanied the report. A bit fuzzy, but it certainly looked like Bhim the Lucky. Who else could it have been?

The next few mornings I scanned the papers for more information on the case. There was a small update, which said that a medical test had confirmed the accused was in his forties. And the woman had disappeared.

Then there was nothing. The newspapers had moved on to other scandals and disasters.

I felt sorry for the woman. We had met only twice, but I had sensed in her a fellow feeling, a shared loneliness that was on the verge of finding relief. But for her it was not to be. I wondered where she was, and what she would do to forget she had given many years of her life for a love that had never truly existed.

I never saw her again.

∽

Not the happiest memory to have of Fosterganj. When I look back on that year, I prefer to think of Hassan and Sunil and Vishaal, and even old Foster (long gone), and the longtailed magpies flitting among the oak trees, and the children playing on the dusty road.

And last winter, when I was spending a few weeks in a bungalow by the sea—far from my Himalayan haunts—I remembered Fosterganj and thought: I have written about moonlight bathing the Taj and the sun beating down on the Coromandel Coast—and so have others—but who will celebrate little Fosterganj?

And so I decided to write this account of the friends I made there—a baker, a banker, a pickpocket, a hare-lipped youth, an old boozer of royal descent, and a few others—to remind myself that there had been such a place, and that it had once been a part of my life.

AFTERWORD: THE WRITER FROM JAMNAGAR

'We are from Jamnagar,' said the head of the family of four who had come toiling up my steps on a cold but sunny Diwali morning. 'Our daughter has one of your books in school, and her teacher says you are the writer from Jamnagar! She would like to pay her respects.'

A smiling girl of about ten stepped forward and shook my hand. 'When were you in Jamnagar?' she asked.

'Eighty years ago,' I told her. 'The first six years of my life were spent there. That's where I learnt to read and write—in the little palace school.'

'That's why you're the writer from Jamnagar,' she said simply. 'And when will you come again?'

'Probably in my next life,' I said. 'It must be a very big city now; I wouldn't find the places I remember.'

'You'll find them,' she said.

Jamnagar! How quaint to be called 'the writer from Jamnagar'. I must say that it gave me a good feeling. I've grown used to being called 'the writer from Mussoorie', although there are a number of other writers who can lay their claim to that title. Jamnagar must have had other, mostly Gujarati, writers to boast of, but in the years from 1934 to 1940, when I was an infant and then a troublesome small boy, the only 'writer' we knew of was Mrs Ghosh, the secretary to Jam Sahib, the state's ruler. Mrs Ghosh was always to be found before Jam Sahib's desk, taking dictation and writing letters to potentates all over the world.

Jamnagar was a small state with a small port and a very rich maharaja, or Jam Sahib as he was called. He owned dozens of Rolls-Royces and an equal number of chauffeurs. He was also a very generous man who, when World War II broke out, gave refuge to several thousand Polish families fleeing from Hitler's storm troopers.

Jamnagar was also the state where Indian cricket was born. So the earlier ruler, Ranjit Sinhji, played for England; a magnificent batsman; so did his nephew, Duleep Sinhji, a master of the glide to leg. And it was on the Jamnagar ground that the great all-rounder Vinoo Mankad won his spurs, going on to make a double century at Lord's, a few years later.

I have memories of the cricket ground in Jamnagar, although not of the cricket. Sitting with my parents in the VIP section, my attention was given over to the steady rotation of trays of sweets—gulab jamuns, rasgullas, jalebis, barfis, savouries of every kind—that circulated among the spectators. How could a small boy concentrate on cricket when all these delicacies kept finding their way into his greedy little hands. No wonder, then, that when I did grow up to play a little cricket, I was inevitably made the twelfth man, carrying out the drinks and refreshments for the rest of the team.

So, what were we doing in Jamnagar just before the war and Indian Independence?

My father was a travelling teacher who, rather than teach in a school, preferred to take up tutorial jobs in the Indian states, of which there were many in those days. He had taught young princes in Bharatpur and Alwar, and at the time of my birth he had moved to the Kathiawar states, doing stints in Jetpur and Pithadia before starting a small palace school in Jamnagar, where we were to live till 1941.

It was a small school, occupying one large room in an old palace, and most of the pupils were girls. I remember them clearly (and still have their photographs): Manha, who was the oldest, about twelve, and quite beautiful; Janak, who was chubby and jolly, always pinching my cheeks; Ratna, serious, thoughtful; and 'Hathi', my age, very sweet and mischievous. These were all princesses. There was also the little prince, the heir to the throne, but I did not see much of him, he was being groomed for a public school, I think. But I do have a photograph of the two of us romping in the sea of Balachadi beach.

The old palace had a turret going up two or three floors, and at the top was a small glassed-in room, each pane of glass a different colour. This was my favourite place. I loved looking through those coloured panes, at the lake or the main palace or the gardens, tinted pink or blue or green or purple or orange. Many years later, I was to write a story centred around this room. It was called 'The Room of Many Colours'. In the story there was an eccentric Rani who gave me sweets, but she was a figment of my imagination. Many of my stories are like that. I start by describing a known place, or persons, and then my imagination takes over and the incidents run away from me.

But this is a memoir, so I must tell the truth.

We had a good cook, but he was not the one who cooked for Jim Corbett while the great hunter was felling man-eating tigers. Our cook made excellent fish cutlets and guava jam, and he ran away with the ayah; but those were the only accomplishments that I can recall.

I should have said that my ayah ran away with the cook, for she was the stronger personality. She reigned supreme in the house. My father never punished me. My mother tried to, but I was too elusive. But there was no escaping ayah's large hands if she was on the warpath. She wouldn't hesitate to bend me over her knee and smack me hard on the bottom. She was fond of me, and in a way, it was a sign of ownership, for she knew no one else would go so far as to give me a good spanking.

I was a funny child. I loved sweeping the veranda steps. I had watched the ayah doing this occasionally, so I borrowed her broom and swept the steps and the veranda whenever they grew muddy or covered with fallen leaves. It gave me a passion for tidiness. I don't sweep verandas any more (just in case you want to hire me for the job), but I like a neat house and my books and papers in the right place. Like Hercule Poirot, if a picture on the wall isn't hanging properly, I'll straighten it.

But I hated haircuts. I dreaded the monthly visits of the unfortunate man who had to cut my hair. I would go into hiding, and when found, would have to be rolled up in a bedsheet and taken, kicking and screaming, to a high chair where my golden locks would be shorn off. On one occasion my mother lost patience with me and let me go halfway through the haircut. For weeks, I went about looking like a cartoon-strip character, long hair on one side of my head and short hair on the other. Today, it would be considered the height of fashion!

I was a nervous, sensitive child. Jamnagar had a small airfield, and one of the princes offered to take my mother and I on a spin in a Tiger Moth, one of those double-winged planes that were then the latest thing in tourist aviation. It was a two-seater, and my mother got in behind the pilot and tried to get me to join her. But I was suddenly overcome with fear. I panicked, and fled from the airfield.

On another occasion, my father took me aboard a dhow, a large sailing vessel that plied across the Gulf of Kutch. It rolled and pitched so much that I demanded to be taken off. I made such a scene that the ship's crew were only too glad to put me ashore, much to the embarrassment of my poor father.

It was a small port with a couple of landing points—

Bedi Bunder and Rosi Bunder. A long causeway went a considerable distance into the sea, and I enjoyed walking up and down this causeway with my parents, watching the seagulls and the fishing boats; but nothing could persuade me to get into a boat.

A small steamer sometimes called at the port, and its captain, a jolly Scotsman, came over to dinner and jokingly offered to take me on a long voyage around the world—Yokohama, San Diego, London. Somehow, I didn't see myself swabbing the deck like Jim Hawkins in *Treasure Island*, but I promised to join him one day. Years later, I put him in an early short story, 'Faraway Places', and called him Captain MacWhirr after the captain in Joseph Conrad's *Typhoon*, one of my favourite stories. But our little tramp steamer would never have stood up to a typhoon; it seemed content to ply up and down the Malabar coast.

I have mentioned *Treasure Island*. There was no bookshop in Jamnagar, and no library that I can recall, and my father's classroom had only a few simple English books. But at home there was a big book of nursery rhymes, and old and well-thumbed copies of *Treasure Island* and *Alice in Wonderland*. And as soon as I could read by myself (without my father's help), I was devouring these books, reading them twice over for want of anything else to read. It was only when we left Jamnagar that I had access to a wider selection of books; and then, hungry for the written word, I would read almost anything that came my way.

There were, of course, comic papers that came my way. Country Commander Bourne's teenage son had them sent out to him from England: *The Dandy*, *The Beano*, *Comic Cuts*, *The Wizard*, and *Magnet* with its stories of Billy Bunter, the fat boy of Greyfriars School. Some of these were story papers, not simple cartoon strips.

Commander Bourne was the state's port authority. He was a genial, hospitable man. Tragically, he developed gangrene due to an injury to his foot. One amputation led to another, but he succumbed to spreading infection. Those were the days before penicillin, and the other antibiotics had not been discovered yet.

Our basic home remedy was 'pinky', crystals of potassium permanganate. When I was badly stung by bees (having disturbed their nest on the steps to the roof of our bungalow), my father bathed my wounds (on my arms and legs) with a solution of 'pinky', and it brought some relief. But the adventure with the beehive taught me to admire nature without interfering with it.

At first, I was afraid of the turkeys in the state farm. 'Gobble-gobble-gobble,' they called, as they clustered around Mr Jenkins at feeding time—their red wattles and pendulous dewlaps were quite alarming at first. But they were a friendly lot, and they had more 'character' than hens and ducks. The geese were quite aggressive, and I gave them a wide berth.

Mr and Mrs Jenkins were a Welsh couple who ran the farm. If I dropped in on them, I could always expect a home-made lemonade and ginger biscuit.

The Jam Sahib employed a number of Europeans and was always very good to their families. My little sister and I were the recipients of numerous toys, dolls, trainsets, teddy bears, Diwali crackers, Christmas puddings.... And there was a car at our disposal. Not a Rolls-Royce, but a sturdy Hillman which opened at the top; ideal for evening drives into the countryside or along the coast.

But most evenings, I sat with my father at the dining table, helping him to sort and arrange his impressive stamp collection. He had albums for different countries, and he arranged and mounted his stamps in sets, according to their date of issue. There were rare stamps from the early days of the Indian and world postal systems, and there were also colourful new issues from small islands and emerging nations. He would deal with philatelists and stamp dealers in Bombay and London, and the well-known Stanley Gibbons catalogues were always at hand. The table had to be cleared for dinner, and sometimes dinner would be late; we were so absorbed in making the albums attractive. My mother wasn't interested in stamps, but she put up with these sessions because they kept me out of mischief.

'One day these albums will be yours,' my father told me, 'so you must know everything about them, especially valuable rarities.'

But when he died in Calcutta five years later, the entire collection vanished mysteriously. But that's another story.

The Jamnagar period was a good time for us. My parents were still in the early years of their marriage, and there was no indication that it was going to break up.

We had a wind-up gramophone and a box full of 78 rpm records. There were nursery rhymes on one of the records, and one of the rhymes went something like this:

Oh, what have you got for dinner, Mrs Bond? There are geese in the parlour and ducks in the pond.

Mrs Bond did not have to worry about making dinner, but she enjoyed making pickles, chutneys, and sauces, and these were usually tested on me before being bottled and preserved. As a result, I became, in time, a collector of pickles. Unlike stamps, they disappear only in one direction. From jackfruits to bitter gourds to sweet lemons to plums, I have had my share of pickles and chutneys, and they still decorate my shelves and dining table.

While my mother was making pickles, and my father was teaching the princesses to read and write, I would be winding up the gramophone, changing the needle and the record, and playing anything from music-hall comic songs to grand opera. My father had a liking for opera, and I listened to it, too, enchanted by the big booming voices of tenors and baritones—Caruso, Chaliapin, Gigli, Tauber. Puccini's operas were very romantic, and some of those lovely arias still linger in my memory. 'Your tiny hand is frozen, let me warm it into life!'

Hard to imagine a frozen hand in the heat and

humidity of Jamnagar, but *La Bohème* and *Madame Butterfly* were my favourites. And the light operas or operettas (now out of fashion) gave us many romantic melodies: Nelson Eddy singing 'Softly, As In the Morning Sunrise', Richard Crooks singing 'Only a Rose', John McCormack singing, 'The Mountains of Mourne'.

Over the years, I have missed those golden voices, but last month little Shrishti searched on her mobile app, and there they all were, resurrected for my benefit! For a couple of hours, I wallowed in musical nostalgia. Technology has its merits.

'Romance brought up the nine-fifteen!' wrote Kipling, and it was the nine-fifteen that took us from Jamnagar to Dehradun, a journey of three days (with changes along the way) in those distant times.

Hitler was rampaging all over Europe, and Britain declared war on Germany. The Japanese army was about to swarm all over Asia, even up to the doors of India. My father felt it was his duty to 'join up', as the expression went, and the Jam Sahib, who supported the Allied war effort, encouraged him to do so.

My father was then in his forties, too old for active service, but he was taken into the Codes and Ciphers section of the RAF. It was the kind of work that suited his temperament.

He joined Air Headquarters in New Delhi (where I was to join him two years later), and my mother, sister, and I went to live with my grandmother in Dehradun. My parents' marriage began to break up soon after, and the outcome was a very turbulent period in my life. It's a story I have told elsewhere.

I did not see Jamnagar again. It's a big industrial city now, I'm told. My memories are of spacious lawns and palaces, small steamers and lonely beaches, and a room with windowpanes of different colours. This childhood helped me to become a writer; so truly, I am a writer from Jamnagar.

Today, eighty years on, it all seems another lifetime.

But I can't help wondering.... What happened to all those turkeys?